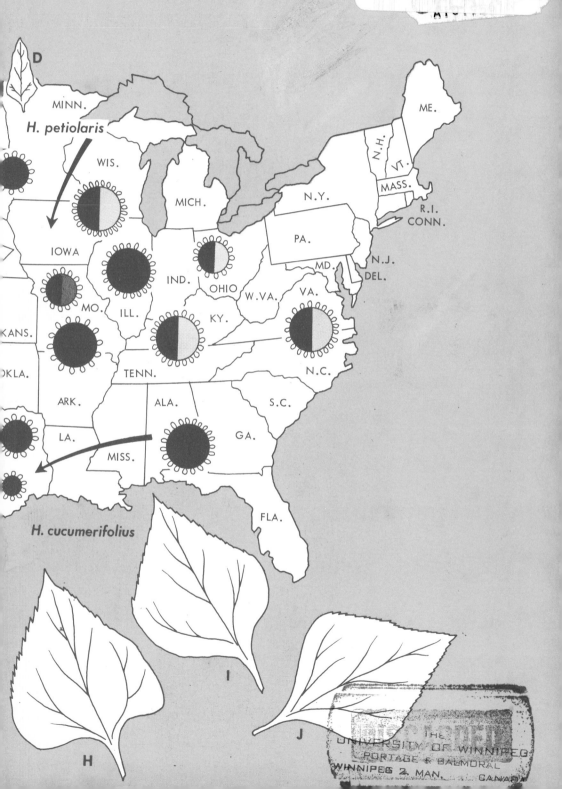

D

MINN.

H. petiolaris

WIS.

MICH.

ME.

N.H.

VT.

MASS.

N.Y.

R.I.

CONN.

PA.

IOWA

IND.

OHIO

MD.

N.J.

DEL.

MO.

ILL.

KY.

W.VA.

VA.

KANS.

N.C.

OKLA.

TENN.

ARK.

ALA.

S.C.

LA.

GA.

MISS.

H. cucumerifolius

FLA.

H

I

J

Principles and Methods of
PLANT BIOSYSTEMATICS

The Macmillan Biology Series

GENERAL EDITORS:

Norman H. Giles and John G. Torrey

THE MACMILLAN COMPANY
COLLIER-MACMILLAN LIMITED, LONDON

Otto T. Solbrig

Harvard University

Principles and Methods
of
PLANT BIOSYSTEMATICS

First Printing

Library of Congress catalog card number: 76–77490

The Macmillan Company,
Collier-Macmillan Canada, Ltd., Toronto, Ontario

Printed in the United States of America

Dedicated to

Angel L. Cabrera
Lincoln Constance
Reed C. Rollins
Benno Ch. Schnack

Preface

Systematics is primarily a comparative discipline, whose objective is to understand the why and how of the diversity of organisms. Most textbooks on systematics stress the classificatory aspects of systematics and neglect to some extent the theoretical and evolutionary aspects of the field. Similarly, most systematic books adequately cover the morphological and anatomical techniques used by the plant systematists, but cover in much less detail the genetical, cytological, chemical, and statistical approaches used in systematic work. The objective of the present text is to present the theoretical and technical aspects of systematics that are not adequately covered in most of the presently available textbooks. This book is designed to be used not only as a textbook in taxonomy courses devoted to the more experimental aspects of the field, but also as a companion to any of the many fine plant taxonomy books being used in introductory courses.

This book assumes a college level course in biology or botany, or a very good biology course in high school. Although a course in genetics is not assumed, such exposure will facilitate understanding this material. Because many students will have had genetics, many common terms are not defined in the text. These terms are, however, defined in the glossary.

The number of different kinds of plants is usually thought to be about 500,000; the number of animal species excluding insects is over a million, while it is estimated that there are two to three million species of insects. Of this tremendous number of organisms, less than a hundred species have been studied so far in anything approaching thoroughness. It is clear that it will never be possible to study all the aspects of the biology of all organisms. Even if such an exercise were possible, it would consume tremendous energies and resources and could not be easily justified in terms of human priorities. It is therefore imperative that our energies be directed toward the discovery and formulation of the basic principles and mechanisms that direct the functioning and evolution of organisms, rather than toward a general survey. Such a selective approach is already prevalent in the more analytical fields such as molecular biology and cellular biology, but is less prevalent in fields such as physiology, anatomy, or systematics. In this book the attitude has been taken that the purpose of science is to establish general principles expressible in rigorous terms. These principles have to be related, however, to the outside world in a direct, precise, and meaningful way; and the reader should satisfy himself that this is so before accepting any generalization. A number of specific examples are presented in the text to illustrate principles. No systematic review of the Plant Kingdom or any part thereof has been attempted. It will be noted, however, that most examples refer to Angiosperms. This reflects my familiarity with the flowering plants, and the fact that more is known about them than about the nonflowering plants. Furthermore, whenever a choice existed, examples have been taken from the most recent literature. The purpose of this action was twofold: first, to show the reader that systematics is a very active field; and second, to allow him to reach the original sources with the least effort. Examples, therefore, are not intended to give credit for the discovery of the principle they illustrate. As a matter of fact, no effort of any sort has been made to present the historical development of systematics except in the brief introduction in Chapter 1.

Many people have aided me in many ways in the writing of this book. Dorothy Crosswhite, Leslie Gottlieb, Harlan Lewis, Robert Ornduff, Reed Rollins, Roberta Solbrig, G. Ledyard Stebbins, and Bill Turner have read and criticized the manuscript in part or in its entirety, making many valuable suggestions, on both content and style, which I hereby gratefully acknowledge. Without their help this book would probably not have been possible. Final responsibility for both content and style is, however, my own. I also want to acknowledge the editorial help and patience of William Eastman and the staff of The Macmillan Company. This work was initiated and finished at Harvard University. It was, however, written for the most part in Ann Arbor, Michigan. I wish to thank the staff of the Department of Botany, the Herbarium, and Botanical Gardens of the University of Michigan, and especially Rogers McVaugh, Alfred Sussman, and Warren H. Wagner, for the use of the facilities of the university, and for the many opportunities for stimulating discussions. The results of these discussions are no doubt incorporated in part in this book.

O.T.S.

Contents

Detailed Contents

Part I

The Process of Speciation and the Forces That Control It

Chapter 1

Introduction and Historical Background

Every science begins with a question about nature that has no immediate answer. Systematics started when man began to wonder about the diversity of living organisms. The first step in a rational attempt to understand the diversity of organisms is to describe and classify them. The second step is to provide a plausible hypothesis for this systematized diversity, and the last, to devise ways to prove the hypothesis. These three steps constitute the basis for the scientific method and mark the historical development of systematics.

This book deals with the principles and methodology of the part of biology primarily concerned with the diversity of plants and their interrelationships. This subject is variously known as taxonomy, systematics, or biosystematics. Because each of these terms has special meanings, we shall first define them as they will be used in this book.

Taxonomy is the study of classification, its principles, procedures, and rules (Simpson, 1961). Classification is the ordering of plants (or any other objects) into classes or groups. It is a very basic, logical operation, because without some sort of initial ordering further comparative studies are made difficult, if not impossible. There are, however, different ways of classifying, and when the objects being classified are living organisms, there are special problems. For example, the leaves of seedlings of many species of *Acacia* are very different from those of the adult plant. Unless all the developmental phases of the plant are observed, there is the risk of classifying the juvenile form as a different species. This risk is even greater among some of the algae, where the various phases of the life cycle look very different from one another; indeed in the past the phases of the life cycle of some species of algae have been described as different species. Such problems do not exist when classifying inanimate objects.

3

The application of distinct names to each of the groups recognized in a classification is known as nomenclature. A set of arbitrary rules has been developed throughout the years. These rules are embodied in a "code" of botanical nomenclature that governs the application of names to plants. Classification, taxonomy, and nomenclature all deal with various aspects of the ordering of plants into some sort of logical system that tries to describe the diversity of living organisms.

Systematics can be defined as that branch of biology that is concerned with the comparative study of organisms and all relationships among them. A relationship can be defined as a statement made about two or more objects that is either true or false. So, for example, a plant may be larger than another, or it may not. Or it can be said that the daisy flower looks exactly like the sunflower. This statement is also either true or false. Such relations are relations of similarity. There are four main types of relationships between plants: (1) Relationships of descent, also called phylogenetic relationships, indicate the degree to which two individual plants are related to a common ancestor. (2) Relations of similarity, known also as phenetic relationships, indicate the degree to which two individual plants look alike, not only in their external morphology, but in all their other aspects, such as anatomy, physiology, and cytology. (3) Spatial or geographical relationships indicate how closely two individual plants are situated to each other, and finally (4) the so-called trophic relations indicate interdependence, that is, the extent to which two individual plants depend on each other; for example, when one is parasitic on the other or when both utilize the same mineral in the soil. Although systematists deal with all four of these relationships, phylogenetic and phenetic relationships are emphasized. In order to ascertain the extent to which two plants are related, one must compare them. Comparison is, therefore, the basic methodological approach of the systematist.

Classifications, although they can be constructed in many ways, have to be based on some kind of relationship among the organisms being classified. Modern classifications of organisms are based on comparative studies, that is, on systematic studies that include all relationships but emphasize phylogenetic and phenetic relations. Since the same person usually undertakes the comparative study and also constructs the classification, systematics and taxonomy are sometimes used as synonymous terms, which they are not.

The term *biosystematy* was first introduced by Camp and Gilly in 1943. They defined biosystematy as an attempt to "delimit the natural biotic units [meaning the units of evolution] and to apply to these units a system of nomenclature adequate to the task of conveying precise information regarding their defined limits, relationships, variability, and dynamic structure." What did they mean by this definition?

Many systematists had been unhappy because existing classifications could not express all the relationships uncovered by systematists. They also felt that the accepted system of nomenclature did not allow a classification that expressed all that was known about the evolution of species. Biosystematics (or biosystematy), as defined by Camp and Gilly, was consequently an attempt to produce a system of nomenclature by which more relationships (mainly phylogenetic relationships) could be explicitly expressed.

However, the term has not always been interpreted as it was originally. Basically it has represented the application of genetical and cytological criteria in systematic studies and, in particular, in the description and circumscription of the basic unit of classification, the species.

Biosystematics is usually interpreted, then, as being essentially synonymous with systematics, although with an emphasis on the study of genetical and cytological phenomena.

Comparison, description, and classification are the first operations that have to be performed in a biosystematic study. Explanation through the formulation of hypothesis is the next, and proving the hypothesis experimentally the last. Actually description and explanation are integral parts of any scientific view of nature. The explanations given by the biosystematist are evolutionary explanations. That is, the relationships between plants are explained within the theory of evolution by natural selection.

Biosystematics can now be defined more precisely as the application of genetics (and cytogenetics), statistics, and chemistry to the solution of systematic questions in order to provide explanations about the diversity of organisms within the frame of the theory of evolution.

In this book the major facets of plant biosystematics as here defined will be presented. In the first seven chapters some of the principal evolutionary problems that concern biosystematists and the questions that these problems pose will be analyzed. The various hypotheses that have been proposed to answer these questions will be presented, as well as the evidence on which these hypotheses rest. In the last five chapters the major experimental approaches of biosystematics will be discussed.

Historical Background

The roots of biology of western civilization are to be found in Greece. However, aside from an awareness of plants and a rudimentary system of classification (plants were classified into herbs, shrubs, and trees), there was little transmitted to modern times in terms of correct specific botanical knowledge: some information about medicinal and poisonous plants and a faint idea about structure, but not much else.

The Middle Ages did not add to the general knowledge. The predominant forms of botanical literature were the herbals, which were books dealing with the imagined economic and medicinal uses of plants. Herbalists copied from earlier works, adding information that reflected the misconceptions of the times and the ignorance of the herbalists. For example, woodcuts of tuberous plants were reversed so that the tubers appeared as fruits, or drawings of man-eating plants were shown. It is obvious that the authors of these works were largely ignorant about the plants they represented in their works. The major concern of the herbalists was with medicine (Lawrence, 1965; Arber, 1928). Their approach was largely based on superstition and preconception, such as the idea held by some that plant parts resembled the human organs that they could help cure.

In the sixteenth and seventeenth centuries and particularly the eighteenth century a reversal took place in these medieval practices and forms of thinking. The changes that occurred and their causes are outside the scope of this book. This was the so-called Age of Reason, and the analytical, rational approach of the times, one that no longer looked at nature with preconceived ideas but with an open mind, was also felt in botany. So, for example, Leonhart Fuchs (1501–1566), who was a professor of medicine in Tübingen, grew most of the plants that he illustrated in his herbals, observing their structures and properties rather than copying from earlier herbals as had been the prevailing custom. This resulted, of course, in more accurate observations and a rekindling of curiosity about plants.

In the following two hundred years the rational approach of the Age of Reason produced a great body of information. First, the native European plants and, later, plants from all over the world were grown in botanical gardens where they were studied and dissected. Chairs of natural science were established in several European universities, and the basic aspects of plants were explored. These studies culminated with the work of the great Swedish naturalist Carolus Linnaeus[1] (1707–1778), and the French school of botanists of the beginning of the nineteenth century. Together they laid the foundations of eighteenth and nineteenth century systematic botany.

Linnaeus and Formal Classification

Linnaeus (Fig. 1–1) was the best known botanist and naturalist of his time. He described hundreds of new species of plants and animals sent to him by correspondents and disciples all over the world. He was Professor of Practical Medicine at Uppsala, Sweden, and founded a famous botanical garden that still exists there today. Two of Linnaeus' books, the *Genera Plantarum* (1737)[2] and *Species Plantarum* (1753), represent a compendium of the knowledge of the day.

Aside from his work in naming and classifying plants, Linnaeus' reputation is based on two major accomplishments. The principal one is the development of the system of nomenclature still in use today. Prior to Linnaeus' time

---

[1] Or Carl Linnè, as he was known in his early years. Linnaeus is a Latinization of the name Linnè.

[2] This work had five editions. For nomenclatural purposes the edition of 1754 is the significant one.

it had been customary in the scientific literature to describe and name plants by short Latin sentences. This system was not the most efficient one. Linnaeus developed a system of naming plants so that a plant carried the name of the genus to which it belonged followed by its own name. The name of the species was a one-word adjective that described some characteristic of the plant. So, for example, the sunflower plant was named *Helianthus annus*,

FIG. 1–1. Portrait of Carolus Linnaeus painted when he was forty-eight years old. (Courtesy: Hunt Botanical Library, Carnegie-Mellon University, Pittsburgh, Pa. 15213. Copied from print in Dörfler: *Botaniker Portrats*, *1907*.)

meaning that it is the annual species of the genus *Helianthus*. This system was adopted because of its simplicity. However, the adjectives chosen to describe the species were not always precise enough, particularly as new species of the genus were described. For example, today there are seventeen known annual species in the genus *Helianthus*. Some later botanists, therefore, changed some of the names given to plants by Linnaeus and others so that they would be more precise. In addition, in many instances plants were redescribed and renamed by botanists who were ignorant of the fact that this had already been done. Indian corn was named *Zea mays* by Linnaeus, but in the next fifty years it was given more than fifteen other names, such as *Zea americana* and *Mayzea cerealis*. This naming and renaming created confusion, because clarity requires that an object have only one name. To alleviate these confusing practices, botanists decided toward the end of the nineteenth century to establish by common agreement certain rules on how to name plants. These rules state, among other things, that the first name given to a plant is the valid one even if it does not accurately describe the plant, as in the case of *Helianthus annus*. The rules make Linnaeus' binomial system of naming plants mandatory, and they further state that Linnaeus' *Genera Plantarum* and *Species Plantarum* are the starting points of plant nomenclature; that is, names published prior to this time are to be ignored.

The other accomplishment of Linnaeus is his sexual system of classification. According to this system the properties of the flower (largely the number of stamens and pistils) circumscribe the major groups of plants.[3]

When studying plants, one soon observes that some have certain characteristics in common. Most of us know without the aid of botanical training what a grass is, or a palm tree. These similarities between certain plants were recognized quite early, and several of our plant families, such as the daisy or sunflower family (Compositae), the carrot family (Umbelliferae), and the pea family (Leguminosae), carry what essentially is a common name given to them before an attempt was made to systematically classify all plants. What characteristics help us recognize members of these families? The process is a complex one, but essentially a whole series of characters of the external morphology of the plant is recognized simultaneously. For example, a palm usually has a straight, relatively thick stem with large and massive leaves borne in a terminal cluster. Grasses are herbaceous, with narrow pointed leaves and no obvious, colorful flowers. A second look at these plants reveals that there are exceptions to most of these characteristics. Bamboos, sugar cane, and corn also are grasses; some palms have no massive stems, some are even climbers. On the other hand, some plants that belong to other families, such as yucca or some century plants, are palmlike; others, such as some sedges and rushes, appear to be grasses to the untrained eye. These apparent similarities present a classificatory dilemma: Should more emphasis be laid on the characteristics of the flowers or on the characteristics of the vegetative parts of the plant?

Linnaeus recognized that the floral parts were more useful than the vegetative organs in grouping like with like. He noted that vegetative characters were more variable, that is, they were more dependent on the vagaries of the environment than floral parts and tended to be related to the environment in which plants grew, so that plants from the same environment had a similar aspect, such as those of the forest being largely trees or shrubs or those of the meadow being all herbs. On the other hand, floral parts usually were quite invariable under different environmental conditions. Therefore, a classification based on similarities of the floral parts reflected more accurately the phylogenetic relationships. Linnaeus did not explicitly state what has just

---

[3] The basic groups were referred to as *orders*, but they are not equivalent to the orders used today.

been discussed; he was not primarily interested in stating phylogenetic relationships. Linnaeus' system was intended primarily to be a key, a device for identifying plants, and not necessarily to reflect natural ordering. Linnaeus, it has to be remembered, lived at a time when most scientists firmly believed that a supernatural being had created plants and animals in their existing forms. It is, therefore, not surprising that his sexual system did not always group plants on the basis of their overall likenesses. For us today Linnaeus' sexual system appears contrived and simplistic. But for his time it was a positive accomplishment because it had the virtue of drawing attention to the reproductive structures of the plant. This focus on the floral parts in turn drew the attention of a new generation of botanists to the reproductive process and phylogenetic relations.

In his classificatory work Linnaeus applied the concepts of formal logic developed by Plato and Aristotle and elaborated during the Middle Ages. In formal Aristotelian logic the basic class is the species. It is a logical class to

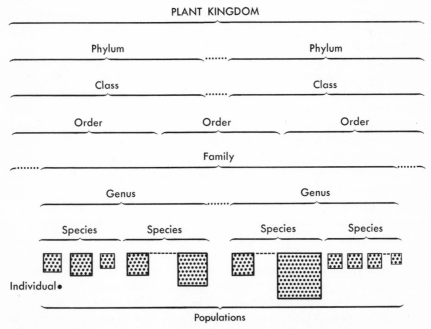

FIG. 1–2. The relation of the various categories of the nomenclatural system. The individual plants indicated by the dots in the squares are the real elements; populations are aggregations of individuals, and are also real elements, although they have certain abstract features (see Chapter 2); species are groups of populations, and are more abstract than populations, although they also have certain real biological attributes (see Chapters 5–7). The categories above species are all abstract, and indicate the existence of certain relations among the elements of a lower order. Brackets are schematic: each category is included in only one category of a higher order.

which belong objects that have certain common properties. Relationships between species can be established by the inclusion of one or more species with some common attributes within another category. Such a system of classification is ideally suited for ordering a large array of organisms (Fig. 1–2). It allows the placement of every plant or animal in a unique species, it makes possible the recognition of each species by a few characters, and it permits the establishment of relationships between the classes through the higher categories. In addition, Linnaeus devised a simple and very useful system of nomenclature (the genus name followed by the species name) that provides an easy way to draw attention to the placement of the species in the hierarchy.

The French School of Systematists

The school of botanists that flourished in France during the last part of the eighteenth and beginning of the nineteenth centuries was not so interested in establishing a system of formal relationships between species as it was in establishing so-called natural affinities. What exactly was meant by *natural affinities* is not entirely clear, and it has been interpreted variously.[4] Basically, however, it was an attempt to study all the properties of the plant and to base the resulting classification on the totality of the characteristics of the plant. That is, there was a greater emphasis on the overall similarity. No a priori judgment was made concerning the importance of particular characters. For example, floral characteristics were not considered more significant for classificatory purposes than vegetative ones until so proved. There was also a greater concern in establishing relationships of descent. This is not to say that Linnaeus was not aware of the importance of heredity or that the French botanists were geneticists; rather, they had a difference in basic outlook. In their so-called natural systems the French botanists and their followers were trying to unravel the fundamental plan that The Creator was supposed to have had in mind in creating the Universe. In searching for the "natural affinities" of plants rather than the formal relationships of Linnaeus' artificial system, the French botanists studied the totality of the properties of the individual, and not only those of direct use in classification. In brief, this outlook was more pragmatic, more objective, and, being perhaps less prejudiced, it permitted in time the formulation of new and more powerful theoretical concepts.

In terms of logic the operations of the French school of botanists would be identified today with the concept of set theory. In set theory a class can be characterized not by the possession of one characteristic shared by all the members of the class as in Aristotelian logic, but by a large number of characteristics. All the members of the class do not necessarily possess all

---

[4] However, the term did not imply "evolutionary," a meaning sometimes given to the term *natural* in present day botanical literature.

these characteristics, but they must have a minimum number. The common chicory is characterized by having blue flowers. Occasionally, however, plants with white flowers are found. If, following classical logical canons in a Linnaean fashion, blue flowers are considered to be a species-specific character, white-flowered plants have to be classed as a different species. However, following the rules of set theory, as long as the white-flowered chicories share all the other characteristics of the blue-flowered ones, they need not be considered as different species. Because the white-flowered chicories are only slight genetic variants of the blue-flowered ones, it can be easily seen in this case that set theory fits the biological picture better than formal logic.

The search for natural affinities foreshadowed an evolutionary explanation, that is, one in which relationships are explained as resulting from descent with modification from a common ancestor. Jean Baptiste Pierre Antoine de Monet, better known as Chevalier de Lamarck (1744–1829), was the earliest of the French naturalists espousing this view with any clarity. Lamarck was the author of one of the first systems in which species were not considered immutable but were supposed to change in time without recourse to some supernatural being. Lamarck failed, however, to produce a plausible mechanism that would effect this change, and in his time his ideas had little impact on systematics.

Charles Darwin and the Idea of Evolution

Until the beginning of the nineteenth century, scientific botany was largely systematic botany even though pharmacology was the most popular aspect of botany at the time. After Linnaeus' time the atomization of the field into a series of subdisciplines began. Morphology, anatomy, cytology, plant physiology, embryology, all developed as independent fields during the nineteenth century. The perfecting of optical instruments, the increase in total knowledge, and the increased professionalization of science that accompanied the Industrial Revolution contributed to this development.

The nineteenth century was also the century of botanical exploration, and the major taxonomic centers of the world received a constant flow of new collections that had to be described and catalogued.

Conceptually, the great development of the nineteenth century was the formulation of the Theory of Evolution by Charles Darwin (1809–1882) (Fig. 1–3) in 1859. He contributed not only the idea of evolution, but the concept of its particular mechanism, natural selection. However, Darwin's theory had an Achilles' heel, and that was the ignorance prevailing in the 1850's concerning inheritance.

Gregor Mendel (1822–1884) was the first to propose the principles of inheritance in 1865. But his work was ignored until rediscovered at the beginning of the twentieth century. The fusion of Darwin's ideas with genetic principles has given rise to the modern theory of evolution. With the addition of the knowledge and concepts of paleontology and systematics, it has developed into the so-called Synthetic Theory of Evolution. The Synthetic Theory is the foundation on which biosystematics rests. It has altered the direction of taxonomic research, because now the diversity of organisms can be not only described but also explained in many instances with a firm basis of theory.

FIG. 1–3. Picture of Charles Darwin taken in 1863, at age fifty-four. (Courtesy: Hunt Botanical Library, Carnegie-Mellon University, Pittsburgh, Pa. 15213.)

Darwin's theory provided a new explanation for an old question, namely, why certain organisms resemble each other more than they resemble others. The observations on which these relationships are based were, of course, not altered by the new explanation; only the interpretation given to them was changed. The Theory of Evolution, therefore, did not immediately alter the methodology of systematics or the results of taxonomic or systematic studies. It was only after scientists started deducing certain conclusions and making predictions from the Theory of Evolution that the general tenor of systematic studies was changed. One of the major aspects of Darwin's theory is differential reproduction. However in Darwin's time very little was known about the facts of reproduction and inheritance. These developments came during the twentieth century and had a profound effect on the methodology of systematics and led to what we in this book describe as biosystematics.

Darwinism had a great impact on the species concept. It produced two major concepts of biosystematic interest that will be discussed in the next chapter; the concept of descent with modification and the concept of the breeding population. Both of these concepts can be tested experimentally at the species level. At higher levels in the taxonomic hierarchy these concepts can be applied only by inference.

The concept of descent with modification implies that the hereditary process is crucial in determining similarities and differences. It is not surprising then that genetic experiments play a major role in modern systematics. The concept of the population means not that the idealized type represents the species, but that all individuals do. Consequently, statistical concepts also play a major role in biosystematics. Finally, modern biology has demonstrated conclusively the chemical nature of life. Chemistry is beginning to play an increasingly important role.

The historical development of systematics can then be summarized as follows. After a first phase of relatively disorganized observations with an emphasis on practical applications, an attempt was made to gather more accurate information about plants and to erect systems of classification. This progression culminated in the eighteenth century with Linnaeus, who provided a system of nomenclature and a system of classification that for a short while was accepted almost universally. The next phase was that of the "natural systems" of the latter part of the eighteenth and the nineteenth centuries. Here the emphasis was on systematic studies that took into account all aspects of the plant. Darwin's theory provided an explanation for the relationships uncovered by the systematists and ushered in a new phase. Finally, in this century, new experimental approaches, particularly genetics, cytology, chemistry, and statistics, permit systematic studies to encompass many more aspects of the biology of the plant than before, and these approaches also allow a certain degree of experimental work.

Let us then turn to a detailed look at some of the principles, concepts, and problems of biosystematics.

Chapter 2

Synthetic Theory of Evolution

The synthetic theory of evolution (see Chapter 1) has never been enunciated in detail because it encompasses many aspects of biology and multiple levels of integration. There are also many ways to study evolution, from the evolution of molecules to the study of the fossil remains of extinct organisms. Furthermore, the factual knowledge of the biological variants at any one level of integration, such as the molecular, cellular, and organismic levels, is still incomplete.

The synthetic theory not only weds the major concepts of Darwinism with new basic concepts that were not known in Darwin's time, but also embraces a series of approaches such as genetics, cytology, chemistry, and statistics that either had not been developed or were in their infancy one hundred years ago.

Basic to the synthetic theory is the concept of natural selection developed by Charles Darwin over a century ago and elaborated and refined over the last forty years by several workers who introduced both genetic knowledge that was not available in Darwin's time and mathematical formulations that helped express natural selection in a more rigorous form.

The concept of population and the redefinition of the species and of the facts of species formation are other important contributions of the synthetic theory. Finally, the dynamics of variability in populations, particularly the genetic phenomena underlying variability and their evolutionary significance, is another highly important aspect of the Theory of Evolution.

The Theory of Evolution provides an explanation for the ancient observation that certain kinds of plants appear to be more similar to each other than they are to others, the explanation being that those plants that are very similar are descended from a recent common ancestor. If so, it should be possible to determine which plants have an immediate common ancestor and which have not. Furthermore, it should be possible to determine the mechanisms that operate through time to transform a common ancestor into two or more different descendants.

Modern systematic studies involve all of the following operations: (1) the description of all the characteristics of plants; (2) the establishment of indices of relationships on the basis of all characters so as to be able to hypothesize the groups that are most related and by inference have a probable common ancestor; (3) the testing of the hypothesis through genetic experimentation and chemical and statistical analysis; and (4) the proposal of the most plausible mechanisms that lead to descent with modification inferred through observation and experimentation.

Let us now look at some of the basic concepts on which the Theory of Evolution rests.

Evolution Through Natural Selection

The principle of natural selection is the cornerstone of the Theory of Evolution and must be well understood if modern biosystematics is to be comprehended. Natural selection, the fundamental law of evolution, is the basic mechanism that makes evolution possible. It was enunciated by Charles Darwin and Alfred Wallace at the same session of the Linnaean Society of London on July 1, 1858. A year later Darwin elaborated his ideas in his now famous book, *The Origin of Species by Means of Natural Selection.*

In its most elementary formulation, natural selection is based on the fact that, given two or more units (genotypes, populations, species) that are capable of self-reproduction, the one that produces the largest number of offspring surviving to reproductive age will be more abundant in the following generation.

One popular definition of natural selection (Lerner, 1958) is "the nonrandom differential reproduction of genotypes." The term "fitness" (sometimes called Darwinian fitness) is used to designate the ability to produce fertile offspring that survive to reproductive age. The best "fit" unit (genotype, population) is the one that produces the largest number of reproductive offspring.

The ways by which a large number of reproducing offspring are produced are varied, and knowledge of them is important to an understanding of the evolution of plants. Basically, however, there are only two major ways for a organism to increase fitness: (1) by increasing the total number of offspring, that is, by increasing the reproductive capacity; (2) by producing offspring that are better adapted to the environment and therefore have a greater probability of survival. Under certain circumstances, one or the other of these two mechanisms becomes prevalent, but basically natural selection tends to maximize both reproductive capacity and adaptation.

Individuals and Populations

One of the major contributions of the Theory of Evolution has been to shift the emphasis in comparative studies from the individual to the breeding population. A breeding population can be defined as a "reproductive community of sexual and cross-fertilized individuals that share in a common gene pool" (Dobzhansky, 1950). This kind of population, called a breeding population or sometimes a Mendelian population, has to be clearly distinguished from the population studied by the statistician or the demographist, who also define a population as a group of individuals but with a different binding property, such as "interaction in space" or "inhabitants of a given geographical locality."

Breeding populations are not necessarily discrete units; often it is hard to draw clear separating lines between them (Fig. 2–1). A good example is the belt of balsam fir, *Abies balsamea*, that extends across northern Canada from Newfoundland to Alberta and from New England to Iowa, sometimes for hundreds of miles with no obvious interruption. How can populations be demarcated in this case? Does the impossibility of delimiting the populations invalidate the concept? No. The inability to differentiate distinct gene pools in certain cases and the overlapping of gene pools in others does not necessarily mean that they do not exist. The problem of delimiting the breeding population into distinct units may be compared to the problem of delimiting young and old organisms. Nevertheless, young and old are useful and valid distinctions.

In asexually reproducing organisms there are no breeding populations, because each individual can reproduce independently. However, most asexually reproducing plants occasionally revert to sexual reproduction. For example, many species of blackberries, genus *Rubus*, reproduce by the formation of seeds without recourse to fertilization (a process known as *apomixis*). However, occasionally some seeds are formed in the normal sexual way by the union of the two gametes, an egg and a sperm. A population of asexually reproducing plants is a breeding population to the extent that it reproduces sexually. In hermaphroditic plants that are capable of self-fertilization, each individual is also capable of independent reproduction, but because in a population of self-fertilizing plants some plants normally outcross, the concept of the breeding population is usually applied also to self-fertilizing organisms.

Mere physical closeness or aggregation of similar plants is not sufficient to constitute a population; there must be some interbreeding. All plants in the population are therefore potential mates. The genes of the parents are combined in the offspring so that the latter usually have intermediate characteristics. Some combinations of genes cause some individuals to have a greater fitness than others. Over the course of time the random crossing of the individuals in each generation will produce many kinds of phenotypes, and those phenotypes that have the greatest fitness will tend to become more numerous, and those that are least fit will tend to disappear. As a result of the combined action of natural selection and the sexual process, and provided that the environment is uniform over the area occupied by the population, the

rrent mutations usually occur with a frequency of 10^{-4} to 10^{-8}. If we
e this rate of mutation by u and the initial gene frequency by p_o, the
r of mutations will be the product of the rate u and the initial fre-
p_o, and the change in the frequency of the gene A_1 in one generation
$-up_o$. But the allele A_2 to which A_1 mutated will in turn mutate back
t a frequency v. If we indicate the frequency of A_2 by q_o we have:

initial frequency of A_1 and A_2: p_o and q_o

mutation rates: $A_1 \underset{v}{\overset{u}{\rightleftharpoons}} A_2$

changes in frequency: $A_1: -u \times p_o$; $A_2: -v \times q_o$

$$\Delta q = u \times p_o - v \times q_o$$

frequency of one allele increases, fewer of the other are left to mutate
direction and more are available to mutate back to the original type.
ally an equilibrium will be reached at which point no further frequency
s will take place as a result of mutation alone. Thus, at equilibrium

$$p \times u = q \times v, \quad \text{or} \quad \frac{p}{q} = \frac{v}{u} \quad \text{and} \quad q = \frac{u}{u + v}$$

e absence of selection the frequency of the gene A_1 depends exclusively
rate at which it mutates to A_2 and on the rate at which A_2 mutates
A_1. Because these rates are very low, as we have seen, the changes that
on alone introduces into a population are very small. Some opponents
idea of natural selection have proposed that mutation alone can
e evolution. However, if there is backmutation, a gene can never
sh itself 100% in a population. Furthermore, a short calculation will
hat in the absence of both selection and backmutation it will take a
um of 5,000 to a maximum of more than 50,000,000 generations, de-
g whether the rate is 10^{-4} or 10^{-8}, to replace half of the A_1 genes by
es in a population. From this we can see that the effect of mutation is
the shorter the span of each generation. So, in a bacterium, 50,000
tions can elapse in less than three years, but in a pine tree it will take
n half a million and a million years. It is clear that mutation per se
ces very little change in the population.

Recombination

netic effect of normal sexual reproduction is to create new diversity in
ploid stage at each generation. The combination when crossing over
tes new combinations of genes at each chromosome; the independent
nent of chromosomes at meiosis creates new combinations of chromo-
in the gametes; cross-fertilization produces new diploid genotypes, and

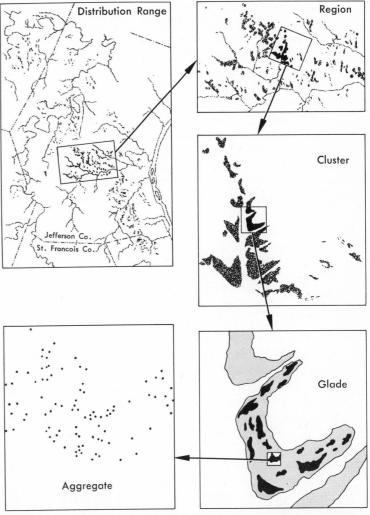

FIG. 2–1. Diagram to illustrate organization of the distribution range of *Clematis fremontii* var. *riehlii* into a hierarchy of subdivisions. This variety is wholly restricted to dolomitic barrens or glades in an area of about 400 sq. miles in east-central Missouri. The taxon, estimated at 1,500,000 plants, is organized into a hierarchy of natural subdivisions: regions of glade concentration; clusters of glades; colonies of the plant that correspond approximately with glades; and aggregates of a very few, to perhaps a thousand plants on each glade (from R. Erickson, 1945).

individuals of the population should tend to have similar genes and also should tend to look quite similar. This situation is usually found in plant populations, lending support to the theory.

Thus, although natural selection favors individual phenotypes and not genotypes, it has a profound effect on the genetic composition of the population. In effect, as a result of the increase of certain phenotypes and the decrease of others, the genotypes and consequently also the individual genes that produce the favored and rejected phenotypes will increase or decrease respectively their frequency in the population. In turn, the changes in frequency of these genes as a result of natural selection determine what genotypes and consequently what phenotypes are produced and their relative abundance. We see then that, because of the mixing action of the reproductive process, over a long period of time natural selection acts on the totality of the genes in the population. This concept is very important.

Evolution at the Population Level: The Forces of Change

From the point of view of genetics, evolution is the change in the frequency of the genes of a population. In order for change to occur there must be at some time a source of new genes. The sources are two: (1) mutation, and (2) introduction of genes from neighboring populations in the form of seeds or pollen (Fig. 2–2). Furthermore, in order to have change there must be a force producing change; the force is, of course, natural selection, although occasionally change occurs solely as a result of chance, a phenomenon known as genetic drift.

Genes do not occur by themselves. They are an integral part of the chromosomes of the plant. Likewise, natural selection does not act directly on the genes, but it affects phenotypes (Fig. 2–2). Through the process of sexual reproduction (recombination), the genes of a population are shuffled and reshuffled in each generation into novel combinations of genotypes that give rise to new kinds of phenotypes. The process of recombination, although it does not give rise to new genes, plays a very important role in evolution through the production of new phenotypes. As a matter of fact, it is so important that recombination and not mutation gives rise to most of the variation that is observed in a population. Let us, then briefly analyze some aspects of these four phenomena: mutation, recombination, natural selection, and gene flow.

Mutation

Mutations, that is, certain changes in the structure of the DNA that result in a modified protein or enzyme and consequently in some modification in the phenotype, are the ultimate source of variation in the population. Many, if not most, changes in the DNA produce changes that are deleterious chemi-

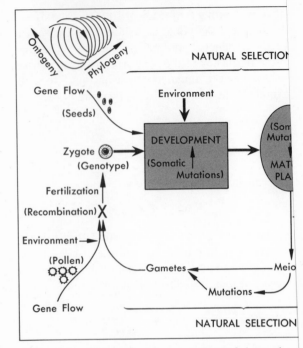

FIG. 2–2. Schematic representation of how the interact. A zygote, the first cell of the organism, is the gametes. It will develop into a mature plant through th process of development (indicated in the sketch as a environmental factors will determine which of the g genotype are finally expressed in the phenotype, t selection is manifested in that some genotypes (zygote ment because of their genetic composition, enviro whereas other genotypes will produce sterile pheno reduced fertility. The mature plant produces in turn with other gametes to produce a new generation of zy fertilization new combinations of genes are produce *recombination*, that result in novel genotypes. Genes c the cycle; however, only those mutations that are gametes will have any lasting effect on evolution. Fina tion of pollen and seeds from other populations, gen complete cycle is known as *ontogeny*; a series of ontog

cally and genetically. Of those that are viable, some be virtually unique. They do not have any permanent because they have an infinitely small chance of survi unless they give a very great and immediate advan highly improbable event. The remaining mutations tions, occur with a measurable frequency. Their eff be assessed mathematically.

Re indic num quen will to A

As in t Eve cha

can produce a virtually endless amount of genetic diversity. This process can produce more numerous and more varied genotypes and at a faster rate than can mutation. Therefore, genetic recombination rather than mutation is the immediate source of variability in a population. Furthermore, adaptations are usually based on complexes of interacting genes and thus recombination is a necessary intermediary, placing mutations in new and varied genetic backgrounds.

The number of diploid genotypes that can be assembled from any number of alleles of a gene is given by the formula

$$g = \frac{r(r+1)}{2}$$

where g = number of diploid genotypes and r = number of alleles at any one locus.

If two different loci, located in different chromosomes so that they can freely recombine, are considered, the total number of possible genotypes that can be assembled for two genes considered together, if each locus has the same number r of alleles, is:

$$g_A \times g_B = \frac{r(r+1)}{2} \times \frac{r(r+1)}{2} = \left[\frac{r(r+1)}{2}\right]^2$$

For example, if it is considered that at each of the two loci there are two alleles

$$r = 2; \quad g_A \times g_B = \left[\frac{2(2+1)}{2}\right]^2 = 9$$

If, instead of dealing with two genes, three are considered, the number of recombinations is given by the product of $g_A \times g_B \times g_C \cdots$ and so on, so that for n genes the number of recombinants will be

$$g_A \times g_B \times g_C \times \cdots \times g_n = \frac{r(r+1)}{2} \times \frac{r(r+1)}{2} \times \cdots \times \frac{r(r+1)}{2}$$

$$g^n = \left[\frac{r(r+1)}{2}\right]^n$$

It can be seen that the number of possible recombinations depends on the number of alleles at one locus (r) and on the number of independent loci (n) and is quite high whenever r and n are over 3, as is the usual case. The number of loci in a genome has been estimated to be in the order of 10^4, and if an average of three alleles per locus in a population is assumed, the number of theoretically possible recombinant genotypes is $6^{(10^4)} = 6^{40}$, an astronomical figure. (There are only approximately 10^{20} stars in the universe!)

However, this tremendous potential for producing variability is only theoretical, because there are several mechanisms that restrict recombination. Foremost is the fact that genes are arranged in chromosomes, so that genes on the same chromosome are not independent as far as assortment to the gametes at meiosis is concerned. Crossing-over can break the linkage of genes in a chromosome, but the frequency of cross-overs is restricted on the average to between one and three per chromosome per generation. Then, although certain loci have as many as 100 alleles (the S or self-incompatibility gene, for example), other loci are monomorphic in a population. Exactly how many genes are monomorphic is as yet unclear, but the number appears to be considerable.

Also, sexual reproduction creates new diversity only when the gametes that combine to form the zygote are genetically different. This diversity can be assumed to happen when the gametes come from different organisms. However, when the combining gametes come from the same organisms, the assumption is suspect. It may or may not be true according to the degree of homozygosis of the plants in question. Inbreeding leads to homozygosis, and the gametes of a homozygous organism are all genetically alike. For this reason sexual reproduction can act efficiently to increase or maintain variability only in genetically heterogeneous cross-fertilizing populations.

It follows that the mode of reproduction of a particular species can give strong clues to the selective situation that favored that species' evolution. The mode of reproduction also determines to a large extent the type of variability of a species. Consequently, before the variability of a species is evaluated for purposes of evolutionary, classificatory, or phylogenetic studies, it is essential that the breeding mechanism be understood.

Selection

Natural selection is the process that accounts for the contribution of varying numbers of offspring to the next generation by the members of the parental generation. The number of offspring an organism contributes to the next generation depends on the ability of the particular genetic makeup of a zygote to interact with the environment in order to produce a phenotype that is capable of growing and reproducing efficiently in the particular physical and biological environment in which that phenotype happens to exist. Most populations tend to go through cycles of expansion and shrinkage in response to favorable and unfavorable conditions. When the population is expanding on account of favorable environmental conditions, most individuals will probably produce some descendants that will survive to reproducing age and will produce some offspring. However, some phenotypes will be producing a relatively greater proportion of offspring than others, and their frequency in the population will increase. When the population is shrinking, on the other hand, because of temporarily unfavorable conditions, a great number of offspring will not survive to reproductive age. It is possible that under such situations no phenotype will show a net increase in numbers. However, in some phenotypes the decrease will be less than in others, and their frequency in the population will increase even if they show no increase in numbers. Finally, when the total population shows no change in size from generation to generation, some phenotypes will be increasing and others will be decreasing. At every instance, then, some individuals may be producing a proportionately greater number of surviving offspring than others. By definition, those phenotypes that show an increase in frequency are being favored by natural selection.

Because of the fluctuations in absolute numbers in the population from time to time, the study of natural selection at all stages and over several generations requires the consideration of frequencies of phenotypes (and their underlying genotypes and genes) rather than absolute numbers. Furthermore, to compare the effect of selection on different members of a population, by convention, natural selection is considered to be always acting against rather than in favor of the offspring of certain organisms, even in those cases where there is no net decrease in the numbers of the offspring.

In sexually reproducing plants the genic makeup of the offspring differs from that of either of its parents. Consequently, it is simpler to study the effect of selection on genes rather than on organisms. However, it should be clearly understood that selection operates on individual organisms and only through them on genes. Only when the differences in fitness between individuals are associated with the presence or absence of a particular gene or group of genes in the individual's genotype does selection operate on that gene and the genotype that contains it. Consequently, the product of selection that affects evolution is determined by the way all of the genes together affect the fitness of an organism.

Most, if not all, new mutations reduce the fitness of the individuals that carry them in a homozygous condition. Many mutations are lethal when homozygous, which means that individuals with a double dose of that gene die. Other mutations are semilethal: most individuals carrying a double dose die, but some survive. And finally, other mutations are subvital: the fitness of the individuals homozygous for it is reduced, but not drastically. In a heterozygous condition, on the other hand, lethal, sublethal, and subvital genes can reduce the fitness of their carriers, be completely neutral (recessive), or even increase the fitness of their carriers. In the first case, there is no dominance for fitness; in the second, recessiveness is complete (because the action of the mutant gene is completely masked); and in the third case, it is an overdominant or heterotic gene. Obviously the behavior of the gene in both the homozygous and heterozygous condition determines its selective advantage or disadvantage in the population. It should be remembered that in diploid organisms, such as angiosperms, when a mutation first appears it will be in a heterozygous condition; its early fate will depend on its effect in this condition. Only when the mutation has become more frequent (as a result of favorable selection or linkage with favored genes) will it become homozygous in some individuals.

It is convenient to remember also that the genes in the chromosomes of an individual interact with each other through the enzymes that each produces, and that the fitness of a particular gene to a certain extent depends on the other genes. So, for example, certain genes are completely recessive in certain genotypes but deleterious in other genotypes. This may be because in the first genotype a gene is present that produces an enzyme that completely inhibits the action of the deleterious gene, but this is not the case in the second genotype. Consequently, a certain fitness assigned to a particular gene refers to the average fitness of that gene in the whole population.

Types of Selection

There are three main forms that natural selection can take: stabilizing selection, disruptive selection, and directional or progressive selection. These three types of selection represent ways by which the population remains adjusted to an environment, which may be either: (1) constant and stable (stabilizing selection); or (2) becoming more variable and breaking up into different subenvironments (disruptive selection); or (3) changing constantly in a single direction (directional selection).

The consequence of selection is usually thought of as phenotypic change. This is not necessarily so and, as a matter of fact, often is not so. Actually, a very common type of selection is *stabilizing selection* (Fig. 2–3). In stabilizing selection, phenotypes with characteristics near the mean of the population are more fit than those at the extreme on account of a stable environment. As a result of this kind of selection, the mean of the population will not vary although its variability may, depending on the genetic determination of the character under consideration.

Blooming period in many spring blooming plants is under stabilizing selection: members of spring blooming species that bloom too early in the season will, on the average, produce fewer seeds than those emerging later, because pollinating insects have not yet emerged; plants blooming late in the season will, on the average, produce fewer seeds than those that bloomed before, because of lack of water or because of competition with other plants.

Another kind of possible selection is one that favors the extremes over the center on account of an environment that is breaking up into two or more types (Fig. 2–3). However, because the extremes breed with each other, in each generation a large number of organisms having the intermediate characteristics will be produced. In an environment favoring the extremes, any mechanisms that would keep opposite extremes from breeding with each other would be highly advantageous, leading to the second type of selection, called *disruptive selection*. Disruptive selection requires some kind of mechanism that ensures that like breeds with like or, in other words, some kind of isolating mechanism.

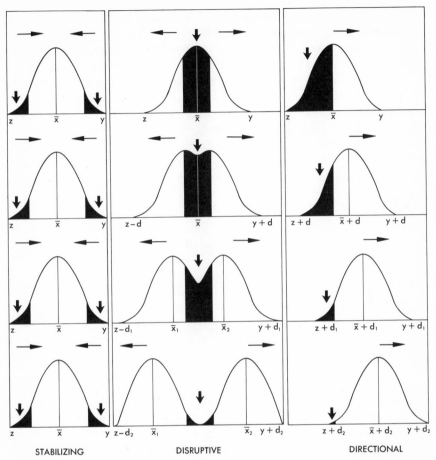

STABILIZING   DISRUPTIVE   DIRECTIONAL

FIG. 2–3. The three main kinds of selection. In stabilizing selection the environment favors the organisms with values close to the populational mean, consequently little or no change is produced in the population; disruptive selection favors the extremes, and will tend to divide the population in two; directional selection favors one extreme, and it will tend to move the mean of the population toward that extreme. Directional selection accounts for most of the change observed during evolution. In the figures the curves represent the frequency of plants with a certain range of values between x and y; the shaded areas, those phenotypes that are being eliminated by selection; the long arrows, the direction of evolutionary change; d = amount of change.

The mechanics of selection that favor the extremes, that is, disruptive selection, are not well understood, and there are no good natural examples that I know. However, an interesting experiment was performed by Thoday and Boam (1959) with *Drosophila melanogaster*. Starting with eight females and eight males that were left to mate at will, Thoday and Boam selected in each generation the four males and four females with the highest number of sternopleural chaetae and the four males and four females with the lowest number. The selected animals were allowed to mate together at will. Because both extremes were equally favored, selection at the beginning was of the stabilizing type with extremes favored. However, by the time the experiment was terminated no more intermediate types were present in the population, apparently because the cross between the flies with high bristle number and the flies with low bristle number produced sterile offspring. Selection had become disruptive rather than stabilizing.

If situations such as the one experimentally produced by Thoday and Boam exist in nature, disruptive selection could be a mechanism leading to speciation. More investigation of this situation is badly needed.

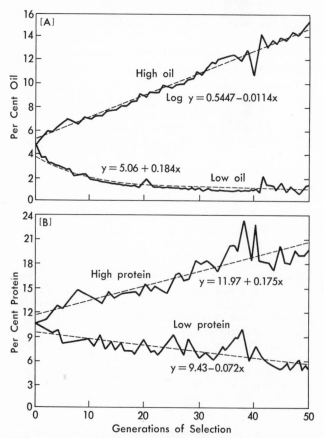

FIG. 2–4. A. Effect of fifty generations of selection on oil content of corn. B. Effect of fifty generations of selection on protein content of corn. Actual data indicated by solid lines; fitted trend lines are shown as broken lines. (From Woodworth, Leng, and Jugenheimer, 1952, *Agronomy Journal* **44**:61, by permission.)

A final kind of selection is *directional selection*. This is the type of selection where one extreme phenotypic expression of a character is favored, which happens in nature when the environment is changing constantly in one direction (Fig. 2–3). Directional selection produces phenotypic and genotypic changes more rapidly than any other kind of selection. Artificial selection is mostly of this kind.

At the Illinois Agricultural Experimental Station, several selection experiments have been performed with corn, *Zea mays*, over the last sixty years (Woodworth *et al.*, 1952). In one of the experiments, plants with ears borne close to the ground were selected in each generation. In the original population the average height of the ears above the ground ranged from forty-three to fifty-six inches in different individuals. After twenty-four generations all the plants produced ears only eight inches above the ground and no more change was produced by selection, presumably because there was no more genetic variability for the determining character. At the same time, in another line derived from the same foundation stock, plants with ears high off the ground were selected. At the end of twenty-four generations the plants produced their ears an average of ten feet above the ground.

In another set of experiments, plants with seeds with high protein content were selected in one line and with low protein content in another. Starting with an average protein content of 10.9%, the high line after fifty generations of selection was producing 19.4% on the average, that is, almost double, and the low line was producing only 4.9%, that is, less than half. In still another experiment, lines were selected for high and low oil content. Starting with plants producing about 5% of oil, a line that produced almost 15% of oil was selected and one that produced only slightly over 1% (Fig. 2–4).

Directional selection probably accounts for the majority of the phenotypic changes that occur during evolution. However, any kind of selection produces genotypic changes by definition. If no phenotypic and/or genotypic changes occur, or if such changes as occur are truly random, no natural selection exists.

Gene Flow

Mutation and selection are phenomena that occur within the population and are not dependent on events occurring elsewhere. Mutation is a random phenomenon that introduces genetic variability at a slow but steady rate, whereas natural selection is the conservative and leveling force that tends to standardize all the individuals of a population at a peak of maximum fitness Inasmuch as most mutations decrease fitness, these two forces work against each other as we have just seen.

Gene flow is the introduction of new genes into a population from outside sources, usually contiguous populations, in the form of occasional crosses between individuals of different populations as a result of the introduction of foreign seed or pollen. In these cases, genes derived by mutation and maintained by selection in a different environment are introduced into the population. The immediate effect is similar to the effect of mutation: a new source of variability in the form of new genes is introduced.

The effect of gene flow is that of a cohesive force within the species that can work counter to selection to a certain extent, depending on the rate of gene flow and the intensity of selection, and that can prevent neighboring populations from becoming too different. Because the effect of gene flow is directly related to the number of immigrants and the intensity of selection, the farther apart two populations are physically and the more their environments differ, the less this cohesive force is felt (Fig. 3–3).

Random Phenomena

So far we have assumed that the population we are dealing with is a very large one (theoretically infinitely large) and that mating is strictly random. Neither of these situations is ever met in nature. All populations are finite, and most are medium-sized and go through periods when their numbers are much decreased, particularly in times of hardship. Likewise, mating is not random; simple factors such as physical proximity, as well as more complicated genetic phenomena such as incompatibility alleles or translocation semisteriles, make random mating impossible.

Reduction in size of the population and nonrandomness of mating makes each generation, to a certain extent, a random sample of the previous one. Consequently, the laws of probability become operative. This means that genes may be eliminated or maintained in a population by chance alone. The probability of a gene's staying or being eliminated in a population is determined by its frequency, which is the result of mutation, selection, and gene flow. Random fluctuations that are not the result of selection can occur in populations from year to year. These will seldom have long-lasting evolutionary effects, but they will keep the population from reaching its theoretical highest fitness. Random phenomena can be of evolutionary significance only when a number of important gene arrangements are completely eliminated from the population. The probability of this occurring, even in populations as small as one hundred individuals, is very low. It is doubtful that random genetic drift, as this phenomenon is called, has ever been a major positive evolutionary force.

Random phenomena do play a role in other ways. Genes that are very low in frequency in a population are not likely to be present in a random sample, and random phenomena consequently enforce selection. This is also the reason why we said before that unique mutations are not likely to have any effect on the population. Random phenomena also play a role in the establishment of new populations, the so-called Mayr's founder principle: the individuals that establish a new population determine the initial frequency of each gene. However, unless the new population becomes isolated from the rest of the species, in time gene flow will tend to bring these initial frequencies into balance with those of neighboring populations. Mayr's founder principle is important in cases such as the colonization of islands and long-range dispersal over barriers such as mountains or deserts.

Mutation, recombination, selection, and gene flow are, then, the basic raw forces whose interaction determines the genetic composition of the population. There are, however, many other factors that determine the evolutionary history of an organism and the diversity of plants at any one point in space. The most important of these factors are the fluctuations in time and space of the physical environment. The environment has been assumed, but not specifically mentioned so far. Let us now look at some relationships of plants and environment, and see how they can be explained in terms of the evolutionary forces that have been reviewed in this chapter and the adaptation to the fluctuating environment.

Chapter 3

Patterns of Phenetic Variability

The comparative study of variability of organisms is one of the major concerns of the systematist and of other students of evolution. The characters of the phenotype are a reflection of the interaction of the internal genetic factors of the plant with the environment. Consequently, it is necessary to assess the extent and types of variability in organisms in order to be able to understand and explain the correlations that exist among phenotype, genotype, and environment. It can be said with little hesitation that the phenotypes of any two plants are different. Each individual in a sexually reproducing population has a distinct genetic endowment that produces different phenotypes. Asexually reproducing plants produce offspring with the same genetic constitution as the parent plants. However, in these cases, because the environment is different from site to site, the plants respond differently and come to differ from each other and their progenitor in spite of having identical genotypes. Variability, that is, the fluctuation of the characteristics of the individuals of a population or species around a mean, is therefore an attribute of all groups of organisms.

Individual plants can differ in any characteristic of the phenotype. The most obvious variations are observed in the external morphology; the least obvious are some basic functions such as respiration and photosynthesis. Variability of these basic functions has not been studied in as much detail as that of morphological characters. However, when physiological aspects of plant populations have been studied, these aspects have also been found to be variable. So, for example, in studies made by Hiesey and his collaborators (Milner and Hiesey, 1964, a, b; Decker, 1959; Björkman, 1966) at the Carnegie Institution of Washington's station at Stanford, California, it was shown that populations of *Mimulus cardinalis* vary in their rate of CO_2 absorption during photosynthesis (Table 3–1).

TABLE 3–1

Photosynthetic Behavior of Three Clones of *Mimulus cardinalis* at Different CO_2 Concentrations. [From Milner and Hiesey, 1964b.]

	Los Trancos, Calif., 45 m	Baja California, Mexico, 550 m	Yosemite, Calif., 1,220 m
Relative maximum rate of photosynthesis with			
0.03% CO_2 concentration	0.65	0.76	0.66
0.0425%	1.00	1.00	1.00
0.150%	2.32	1.87	1.90
Performance index with			
0.03% CO_2 concentration	—	—	89.3
0.0425%	94.7	94.5	81.9
0.150%	67.6	65.4	49.6

In another recent study, McNaughton (1965) investigated differences between populations of *Typha latifolia*, the common cattail. McNaughton studied the activity of an enzyme, glycolic acid oxidase. The exact role of this enzyme is not entirely clear, but it is known that it is an important element in carbohydrate metabolism. Differences in enzyme activity consequently ought to be of direct adaptive value to the organisms. Four populations were selected for study: two from sites near Beavarton, Oregon, in a semimaritime climate characterized by a long growing season (264 days) with cool midsummer high temperatures of about 25°C and mild midsummer low temperatures of about 15°C. The other two populations were from Redmond, Oregon, a locality that has a continental climate characterized by a short growing season of only 130 days with warm midsummer high temperatures of approximately 35°C and low, cool midsummer temperatures of about 10°C. The mean temperatures of the two localities were similar, but the diurnal variation is much greater at Redmond than in Beavarton.

Table 3–2 shows the results of the experiments conducted at three different temperatures. It can be seen that both Beavarton populations, but particularly population A, showed higher activity than both Redmond populations. The sole exception was Beavarton B, which showed statistically significantly less activity at 37°C than Redmond A.

These studies clearly show that plants vary probably as much in their physiological characteristics as they do in their morphological attributes. However, until now most studies of variation have emphasized morphology for the simple reason that characters of the exterior morphology of an organism are easier to observe and quantify.

In this chapter we will analyze some of the patterns of phenotypic variability that are commonly encountered among plants, and we will try to present the known facts and the general hypothesis concerning the causes that produce those patterns of variability.

TABLE 3-2

Glycolic Acid Oxidase Activity in Chloroplast Fragments from Ecotypes of *Typha latifolia* at Three Temperatures, Expressed as Mililiters of Oxygen Consumption in 5 Minutes. [From McNaughton, 1965.]

	Oxidase Activity			
	Beavarton		Redmond	
Temperature [°C]	Pop. A	Pop. B	Pop. A	Pop. B
17	31.9	18.8	8.9	8.7
27	30.0	16.3	11.8	9.9
37	19.9	9.7	12.6	9.2

Geographical Variability

One of the most common patterns of variability encountered in nature is one that correlates with geography. An example is a shrub, *Gutierrezia sarothrae*, commonly known as snakeweed. This low, globose shrub in the Compositae, the sunflower family, grows from the western edge of the prairies in North America to the Pacific Ocean and from northern Mexico to Alberta and British Columbia in Canada (Fig. 3–1). It is not found growing continuously over this area, however, but it forms very discrete, widely scattered breeding populations formed by fifty to one thousand plants or more. These populations are separated from each other by anywhere between a few hundred yards to tens and even hundreds of miles (Solbrig, 1964).

In order to gain an idea of the degree and the pattern of variability in these populations, eleven morphological characters were measured in each of fifty plants from every one of fifty-three natural populations. Most populations differed from each other in the mean value of the measured characters in a statistically significant way. However, there was overlap in most cases as far as the range of variability was concerned (Table 3–3). The most striking example is offered by the number of flowers in the inflorescence, called a *capitulum* or *head* in the Compositae. In samples of fifty plants from single populations, the number of ligulate flowers varied from two to seven and the number of tubular flowers from zero to seven. Traditionally, this character has been considered very important in the characterization of species in the family Compositae.

The value of the mean for some of the characters measured was correlated with geography. For example, plant height (Fig. 3–2) is correlated with: (1) latitude: other factors being equal, northern plants are shorter than southern ones; and (2) longitude: other factors being equal, plants growing west are larger than plants growing east. However, factors other than distribution in space are also correlated with plant height. Within the same latitude, plants of *G. sarothrae* of higher altitudes are shorter than those of lower altitudes.

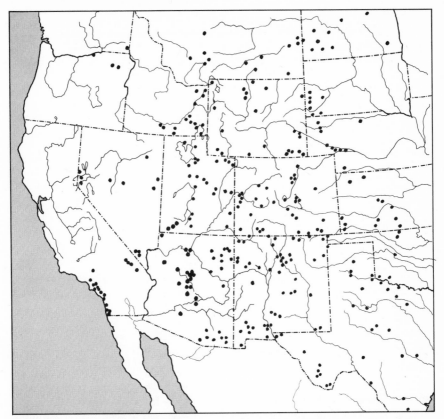

FIG. 3–1. Geographical distribution of the "snakeweed," *Gutierrezia sarothrae*, in the United States. Each dot represents a known population; other populations no doubt exist, but it is unlikely that the pattern here represented would be much altered by the addition of the unknown populations. Note how certain populations, particularly those at the fringes of the distribution, are relatively isolated; note also how rare the species is in parts of Nevada, Idaho, and Wyoming. (From Solbrig, 1964.)

On the other hand, other characteristics measured, such as number of flowers per head, were not correlated with geography or, if a correlation existed, it was not absolute.

Gutierrezia sarothrae illustrates a pattern of variability that is found to a greater or lesser extent in most species that are distributed over a large and ecologically diverse area. This is a pattern of correlation of the variability with geography for some characters, but not all.

The general hypothesis regarding the reasons for the differences that are observed among breeding populations over a large area is as follows. Individual populations are subjected to environments that vary from population to population. Consequently, the phenotypes that are favored by natural

TABLE 3-3

Comparison of Nine Characters of Diploid and Tetraploid Plants of *Gutierrezia sarothrae*.
[From Solbrig, 1964.]

Character Examined	Range		Mean		t* [P0.05–1.96]
	Diploid	Tetraploid	Diploid	Tetraploid	
Plant height	4–38	4.5–28	10.93	10.13	0.942
Involucre height	2.5–5.0	2.6–6.2	3.77	3.56	0.075
Involucre width	0.9–2.9	1.1–2.7	1.77	1.81	0.031
Tubular flowers	0–7	0–7	3.67	3.90	1.118
Ligulate flowers	2–7	3–6	4.87	4.49	0.851
Tubular pappus length	0.5–2.0	0.6–2.0	1.24	1.31	0.076
Lig. pappus length	0.2–1.2	0.4–1.3	0.58	0.73	0.333
Pollen diameter	9–16	11–17	12.57	13.59	2.930
Stoma length	14–24	15–25	18.13	19.97	1.870

* A value for t less than 1.96 means that the difference between the diploid and tetraploid plants is not statistically significant at the 5% level, or in other words, the probability of error in considering the populations different, is more than 5%.

selection at one site are not necessarily favored at another site. That is, evidence from observation and transplant experiments indicates that natural selection will favor different phenotypes in different areas. On each site, certain characteristics of the phenotype are of more direct adaptive value than others. These more important characteristics are the ones that will show the strongest correlation with geography. However, the transmission of pollen and seeds from one population to another will introduce genes from neighboring populations. These introduced genes will tend to be eliminated in the new host population unless they contribute to its total fitness. If the rate at which they are eliminated is slower than the rate at which they are introduced, gene flow will prevent the populations from diverging significantly. Gene flow in this case acts as a cohesive force within the species.

On the other hand, if gene flow becomes negligible or is completely eliminated (because of the distance between populations, for example), the rate at which natural selection proceeds is accelerated. Spatial isolation has also been considered as a first necessary step in the speciation process as we will see further on (Fig. 3-3).

The hypothesis of geographical variability is simple; however, the natural situation is highly involved, and the demonstration of the hypothesis is quite difficult in specific cases. The basic variables, time, space, gene flow, and intensity of selection, are not correlated. Furthermore, in most cases only space can be measured among the variables. Time since establishment of the population is almost impossible to determine in most cases, and estimates of gene flow and intensity of selection have so far been very hard to obtain.

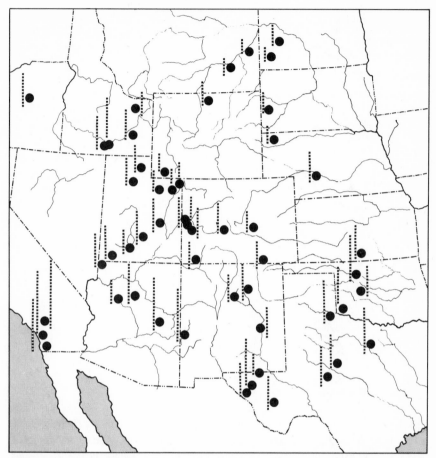

FIG. 3–2. Average plant height of populations of *Gutierrezia sarothrae*. Each division of the bar represents one inch. Note how northern populations are generally shorter than southern ones, and how western populations on the same latitude are generally larger than eastern ones. (From Solbrig, 1964.)

Consequently, the biosystematist is usually faced with the following situation. A careful analysis via a statistical description of the phenotypes of the population (morphology, anatomy, chemistry, and so on) establishes that there is variation. But, unable to determine the intensity of selection or the degree of gene flow, the biosystematist analyzes the geographical picture and the broad features of the environment looking for correlations. These trends are then interpreted in terms of selection, as in the example of *Gutierrezia sarothrae*.

However, this general approach is not sufficient for an understanding of the dynamic picture. Measuring plants in the field, no matter how carefully, only reveals the phenotypic differences, and these are due to an interaction

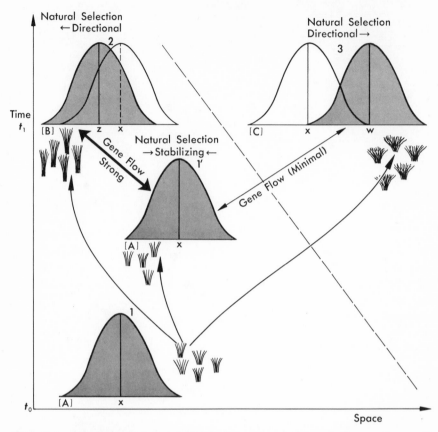

FIG. 3–3. This pictorial graph illustrates some of the evolutionary forces at work in a situation involving geographical variation in space and change in time. At time t_0, population 1 was adapted and growing at site A with a mean x (to represent a mean of all character states). At time t_1, population 1 has given rise to populations 1′, 2, and 3 at sites A, B, and C. At B natural selection favors a mean z, at A it favors still a mean x, and at C a mean w. A and B being very close and environmentally similar, gene flow is strong, and directional selection not very different, the opposite is true for C.

between genotypes and environment (Fig. 2–2). A necessary step is to deter-mine the extent to which the differences are heritable. This determination is accomplished by growing plants from various geographical sources under a uniform environment, preferably under several such uniform environments. Phenotypic differences can now be assumed to represent genetic differences. Crosses between the populations can then be performed to test the inheritance of the characters under study. Furthermore, the performance of the hybrid can be used as an estimate of the effect of gene flow (e.g., are the hybrids weak or vigorous?), as well as the degree to which populations have differentiated in regard to genetic isolation barriers (how much seed does the hybrid produce?). Finally, a careful analysis of the local environments should reveal more features to which the local population may be closely adapted. Such studies are time consuming and require special facilities, such as transplant stations, growth chambers, and so on, that are not always easily available. When these studies have been performed they have revealed that the differences between populations of the same species, particularly physiological differences, are always of a greater magnitude than would be expected from a cursory analysis.

Transplant Experiments

The Swedish botanist Göte Turesson (1922, 1925, 1929) was one of the first to apply the transplant method of study to geographical variation. He assembled plants from diverse environments at the experimental garden of the Institute of Genetics at Åkarp, Sweden. Species having a wide and continuous geographical distribution over a variety of climates were selected for study. The samples were formed of twenty or more individuals to obtain a fair idea of the variation within each population. By comparing such collections in a standard environment, Turesson obtained an insight into the phenomenon of geographical variation.

Physiological characters such as time of flowering were especially emphasized. He found that, in general, southern European, Alpine, and high Nordic populations were first to bloom at Åkarp, whereas lowland forms from northern and central Europe were the last to bloom. He was also able to demonstrate that certain morphological types tend to be associated with particular habitats. For example, Alpine forms in general were dwarf and lowland types were tall, whereas plants growing at the seashore were often characterized by a prostrate habit and thick, fleshy leaves. Forms from southern latitudes were, as a rule, taller than plants from the far north, which resembled the Alpine forms in height.

As a result of his studies, Turesson proposed the concept of ecological race or ecotype, also known as genetical race or simply race. The basic concept suggests that at a given locality the local populations possess particular heritable physiological characteristics that make them better adapted to the local environment than populations from other localities, and that species are composed of different races.

The Experiments of Clausen, Keck, and Hiesey

The concepts and ideas introduced by Turesson were thoroughly tested and developed further in one of the most complete and thorough studies of variability, which was performed by the team of Jens Clausen, David Keck, and William Hiesey over a period of nearly thirty years. These investigators established, under the auspices of the Carnegie Institution of Washington, three transplant stations in California at approximately 38°N latitude. The first is located at Stanford near the San Francisco Bay. It has a mild coastal climate, the altitude of the station is only 30 m, and although mild winter frosts do occur, in general conditions are favorable for a considerable amount of growth even during the winter, because the minimum temperature remains relatively high. Winter conditions are much less likely to hinder growth at Stanford than are the heat and drought of the summer. The second station is located at Mather, at 1,400 m elevation on the west slope of the Sierra Nevada. In Mather the climate favors active growth of plants only during the period between May and October. Spring weather ordinarily begins the first part of April, although frost may occur until the beginning of June. The summers are mild with warm days and cool nights and little rain. The fall is cool and dry. Snow can be expected between October and April, rarely exceeding two or three feet in depth. The third station is located at Timberline in the Sierra Nevada at 3,050 m. Here the climate is quite severe, with only three to six weeks of frost-free weather during the year and no assurance that a frost may not occur at any time. The snow may accumulate ten to twenty feet in the winter.

The extensive investigations of Clausen, Keck, and Hiesey (1940, 1945, 1948) and Clausen and Hiesey (1956) on a series of western North American plants have demonstrated the existence of local races in certain species at least. Especially thoroughly investigated were *Potentilla glandulosa*, several species of yarrow, *Achillea*, and species of the subtrite Madineae of the Compositae. Plants from different geographical areas were brought from the field, divided into three clones, and one planted at each of the three stations. Physiological and morphological characteristics of the plants brought to the three stations were recorded. The observations of Turesson were confirmed. It was also shown that plants originally from lowlands usually did not survive at Timberline and that plants from the high altitudes likewise grew poorly or not at all at the low elevation (Fig. 3–4). This was true even among populations of the same species. Crosses between these different populations showed that the differences were genetically determined and that they constituted ecotypes in the sense of Turesson's definition.

A very fine example of these investigations is the thorough study of the variability of *Potentilla glandulosa*. This is a species of herbs that belongs to the rose family, Rosaceae. It is formed by a series of local populations scattered widely through western North America. A great number of populations from California were sampled by the team of Clausen, Keck, and Hiesey. The species can be divided on the basis of morphology into four subspecies: subspecies *glandulosa* occupies the coast ranges of California and isolated localities in the foothills of the southern Sierra Nevada; subspecies *reflexa* occurs on warm, sunny slopes of the foothills and mid-altitudes of the Sierra Nevada from 300 to 2,000 m elevation. Subspecies *hanseni* is a meadow form

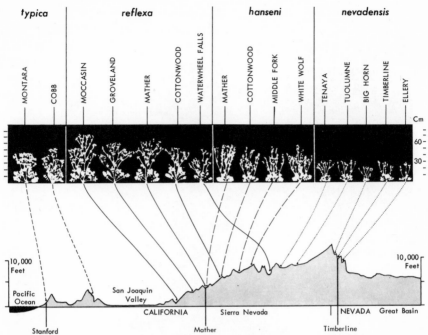

FIG. 3–4. Silhouettes of herbarium specimens of sample plants of *Potentilla glandulosa* of the four subspecies grown at Stanford under uniform conditions, with a profile across central California at approximately 38° north latitude, indicating the original localities of the populations. Note how the morphology of the plants becomes modified from east to west, and also note that ssp. *reflexa* and ssp. *hanseni* overlap in part of their range. The profile map also indicates the position of the three transplant stations at Stanford, Mather, and Timberline. (Modified from Clausen, Keck, and Hiesey, 1940, by permission.)

occurring between 1,300 and 3,000 m altitude; and finally subspecies *nevadensis* is a high-altitude meadow or slope form that occurs from 3,000 to 3,600 m altitude. The subspecies of *Pontentilla glandulosa* have no barriers to interbreeding except those provided by their spatial and ecological separation.

Samples from several populations from each of these subspecies were grown at the three transplant stations in Stanford, Mather, and at Timberline with the following results. The coast range form of subspecies *glandulosa* grew tallest at Stanford, less well at Mather, and failed to survive the winter at Timberline (Fig. 3–5). Subspecies *reflexa*, on the other hand, grew best at Mather, where it is native, less vigorously at Stanford, and also died at Timberline. Subspecies *hanseni* was strongly winter dormant at Stanford (even though the winters are mild), grew best at Mather, and survived at Timberline, although it was seldom able to set ripe seed at the high altitude. Finally, subspecies *nevadensis* barely survived at Stanford, where it also was winter dormant; it was most vigorous at Mather, and it was vigorous and

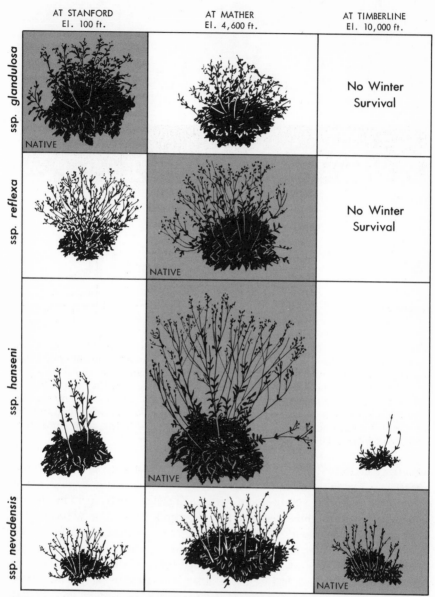

FIG. 3–5. Responses of four ecotypic subspecies of *Potentilla glandulosa* to the three contrasting environments in the Carnegie Institution gardens at Stanford (left), Mather (center), and Timberline (right). The four subspecies are: *nevadensis* from 10,000 feet elevation (bottom row), *hanseni* (second row from bottom), from 4,600 feet; *reflexa* (third row from bottom), from 2,500 feet in the Sierra Nevada foothills; and *glandulosa* (top row) from 900 feet in the Outer Coast Ranges of California (see Fig. 3–4). (Modified from Clausen, Keck, and Hiesey, 1940, by permission.)

consistently set seed at Timberline. We see, then, that the four morphological subspecies also represent four distinct physiological types. Furthermore, each one performed best in terms of growth and seed set at the station that was closest to its native environment, with the exception of subspecies *nevadensis*, which did better at Mather than at Timberline. However, subspecies *nevadensis* was the only one of the subspecies capable of functioning normally in the extremely harsh conditions of the Timberline station.

The Experiments of Macmillan

Macmillan (1959, 1964, 1965) has studied the nature of the grassland communities of North America in the same fashion as Clausen, Keck, and Hiesey for a number of years. Particularly pertinent is a study of the behavior of hundreds of clones of four species of grasses: *Andropogon scoparius*, *A. gerardi, Panicum virgatum*, and *Sorghastrum nutans*. Populations from as far north as Michigan and New England and as far south as Mexico City were sampled and grown under uniform conditions in the experimental garden at the University of Texas at Austin, Texas. Macmillan found that there were indeed hereditary morphological and physiological variations between clones from different geographical regions (Figs. 3–6 and 3–7). In general, these did not form well-delimited groups, but rather tended to intergrade slowly into each other. These variations were clearly adaptive. For example, the northern clones (Massachusetts, Michigan, Wisconsin) were of shorter stature and were early-blooming whereas the plants of southern clones (Texas, Louisiana) were taller and late-blooming. It was hypothesized that, under the climatic pattern of northern habitats with relatively few frost-free periods of growth, selection favors a developmental pattern geared to maintaining the populations through rapid growth and early flowering. In the southern climates, on the other hand, the growing season is much longer. In this situation the interpretation of the greater stature of southern grasses is that there is a competitive advantage for the plant that can grow taller and capture more of the sun's energy. There probably is also an advantage in shading (and killing) smaller plants. During the long growing season of southern regions, plants probably receive selective advantage by continuous vegetative growth (and consequent larger size) and late blooming. Plants in northern communities with such a growth pattern are eliminated by frost.

The concept of the very distinct ecological race is not as easily applicable to prairie grasses as it is to certain Californian plants that grow in very distinct ecological regions that do not intergrade. However, the basic concept that species are formed by a series of more or less locally adapted populations seems to be confirmed. The answer to the problem of how these local races can originate in the presence of gene flow from other populations has two alternative solutions. One hypothesis is that there must be very little gene flow when the local races are being formed. The second hypothesis is that

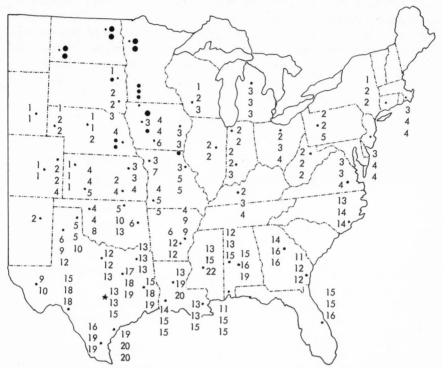

FIG. 3–6. Flowering of transplanted clones of *Panicum virgatum* at Austin, Texas (indicated by a star). Numbers indicate weeks after April 27, 1961, for the first plant to bloom in each clone. Large circles indicate that the plants from those localities never bloomed. (From Macmillan, 1965, by permission.)

selection is sufficiently intense so that gene flow is not an important consideration. These hypotheses are not mutually exclusive, and all combinations of degree of gene flow and intensity of selection can be visualized as leading to the formation of local races.

In some cases, such as in California, the geographic and physiognomic situation is such that it creates disjunctions for a given species, e.g., the central valley of California separates the coastal race, subspecies *glandulosa* of *Potentilla glandulosa*, from the foothill race, subspecies *reflexa*. In many other cases sharp climatic boundaries exist that are not so obvious as the geographic ones, but are equally effective in checking gene flow. So, for example, Macmillan states that the region south of a line drawn from southern Virginia through North Carolina and westward through Tennessee, Arkansas, Oklahoma, and across the Texas panhandle is one with a mean daily temperature permanently above 35°F. Directly north of this line is a very narrow band with winter temperatures below 35°F but with a slow rise during February, March, and also April to the higher summer temperatures. North of this

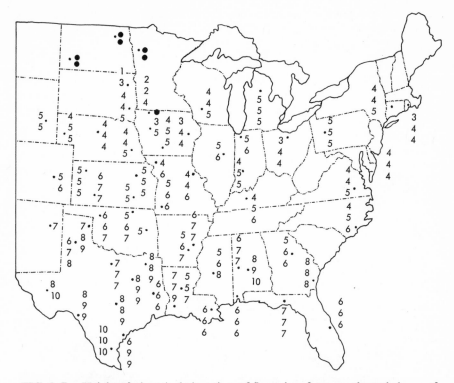

FIG. 3–7. Height of plant (culm) at time of flowering, for transplanted clones of *Panicum virgatum*, grown in Austin, Texas, during 1961. No. 1: 1–25 cm; 2: 26–50 cm; 3: 51–75 cm; 4: 76–100 cm; 5: 101–125 cm; 6: 126–150 cm; 7: 151–175 cm; 8: 176–200 cm; 9: 201–225 cm; and 10: over 225 cm. Large circles indicate that the plants of those localities did not bloom. Note the great difference in size between northern and southern plants. (From Macmillan, 1965, by permission.)

area, however, a broad belt reaches 35°F in late spring over a relatively short period, as anybody who has witnessed a New England "spring" knows. Such steep climatic changes are as important in checking gene flow as are geographic barriers. In this case it is certainly a significant factor in the geographic separation of northern, early-maturing grass ecotypes from southern, late-maturing ecotypes.

It should be clear that one of the problems in the formulation of a general model of geographical variation is how to assess correctly the relative role of gene flow and the intensity of natural selection.

Genotype-Environmental Interaction

Plants are phenotypically quite variable as every gardener knows. Such environmental components as light, water, temperature, and soil, to name just a few of the most important ones, can drastically affect the characteristics of a plant (Fig. 3–8). That these effects are environmentally induced has been repeatedly demonstrated.

Clausen and collaborators have been investigating for a number of years the effects of the environment on similar and dissimilar genotypes. Watson and Clausen (1961) have reported the results of such studies on species of the grass genus *Poa*. Many species of this genus are apomictic, that is, they

FIG. 3–8. Phenotypic plasticity of a plant of *Glandularia canadensis* from Oklahoma. Six cuttings were made from the original plant (assuring an identical genotype) and placed (from left): 1, in high humidity, low light intensity, and ambient temperature; 2, in high humidity, high light intensity, and ambient temperature; 3, in normal humidity, low light intensity, and low temperature; 4, normal humidity, high light intensity, and low temperature; 5, normal humidity, low light intensity, and ambient temperature; and 6, normal humidity, high light intensity, and ambient temperature. Note the great phenotypic variability, all produced by the same genotype, growing in different environments. (Courtesy of P. Sharma.)

reproduce by seeds that are formed asexually. However, these apomicts are facultative, meaning that some seeds can be produced by sexual means in each generation. Taking advantage of this fact, a cross between two related species, *Poa ampla* and *P. pratensis*, was produced. From the offspring of this cross (which reproduced entirely by sexual means) several apomictic lines were selected. The offspring of each of these lines was genetically identical or almost identical, because they were produced without recourse to fertilization. These were then grown and studied at three distantly located places, after

TABLE 3-4

Comparison of Poa Hybrid and Apomictic Lines Grown at Three Different Localities. [From Watson and Clausen, 1961.]

Center	Character	Parents		Lines				Center
		pa	pp	S-23	S-309	P-507	E-701	Average
Pentlandfield 1957–58	Stem length	100.0	81.7	77.4	84.9	93.4	85.2	87.1
	Stem number	115.4	107.7	93.7	100.3	50.9	116.4	97.4
	Basal width	11.1	55.2	45.8	48.4	40.9	40.8	40.4
	Vigor	7.6	7.6	8.4	7.5	6.6	6.7	6.1
	Flowering date	12/VI	23/V	10/VI	30/V	3/VI	21/VI	7/VI
Pullman 1956–57	Stem length	83.7	86.7	75.0	83.3	104.1	73.7	84.4
	Stem number	153.3	391.0	207.0	316.5	369.1	260.5	289.9
	Basal width	13.4	44.8	27.5	25.8	34.2	28.5	29.0
	Vigor	5.9	7.7	5.5	6.9	8.2	6.2	6.7
	Flowering date	31/V	6/V	1/VI	26/V	20/V	28/V	18/V
Stanford*	Stem length	69.2**	76.8	58.8	81.9	82.8	38.8	68.1
	Stem number	69.2**	132.1**	53.3	61.5	99.0	30.0	72.5
	Basal width	12.1**	34.3	22.7	23.6	27.6	38.5	26.5
	Vigor	4.2**	5.2	5.3	6.8	6.9	4.9	5.6
	Flowering date	23/V**	13/IV	21/IV	15/IV	16/IV	12/IV	22/IV

* Values taken in different years between 1950 and 1958.
** Not many plants survived for measurement.

45

being divided into three equal sets of seeds. The first station was the experimental garden of the Carnegie Institution of Washington at Stanford, California, U.S.A., located at 38°N latitude. The second station was the Soil Conservation Service Nursery at Pullman, Washington, U.S.A., situated at 46°N. The altitude here is 300 m and the winters are moderately severe, including some very low temperatures. The third station was the experimental garden of the Scottish Plant Breeding Station at Pentlandfield near Edinburgh, Scotland, at 56°N. The altitude here is 200 m, and growth is favored during spring, summer, and autumn only, the average winter temperatures being lower than at Stanford in spite of relatively mild winter temperatures.

The parental species have very different characters. *Poa ampla* is a rather variable species native to the Pacific Northwest of North America. It is a very tall-growing, winter-active bunch grass. *Poa pratensis* has a very wide distribution throughout the northern hemisphere. It is not as robust as *P. ampla*.

Table 3–4 shows the mean of four characters measured and the date of flowering at the three stations for the parental species and four apomictic hybrid derivatives. Several important points are demonstrated. First, identical or almost identical genotypes produce dissimilar phenotypes when grown under different conditions. Second, related but different genotypes behave differently under the same environmental conditions, as seen by the four lines selected from the F_2 of the *Poa ampla* $\times$ *P. pratensis* cross. And finally, different characters are affected in different ways by the environment. For example, in the line E-701 the number of stems was considerably larger when the plants were grown at Pullman (260.5) than when grown at Pentlandfield (116.4). At Stanford the number was considerably smaller (30.0). However, the stem length was about the same in Pentlandfield (85.2) and in Pullman (73.7), but again much smaller at Stanford (38.8).

Plasticity

The phenotypic variability (plasticity) of plants probably has a great survival value, because it is such a universal phenomenon. It is a phenomenon that is largely peculiar to plants, because animals, particularly the higher vertebrates, maintain their phenotypic characteristics much more constantly than plants when put in different environments. Phenotypic variability is usually interpreted as a response to the environment (Fig. 3–8). If so, it would be expected that organisms such as plants, which cannot move and therefore cannot avoid the environmental rigors of the place where they happen to germinate, would show the greatest degree of phenotypic variability. It is of interest to note also that even animals, for instance squirrels, respond to those factors of the environment that they cannot avoid, such as low temperatures and meager resources in winter, by a somewhat similar change in the phenotype, e.g., accumulating winter fat, acquiring long fur, and hibernating.

Natural selection cannot influence characteristics that are not inherited, as we saw in the previous chapter. Phenotypic modifications are by definition noninheritable, and therefore it would appear that they cannot be the result of selection. However, as Clausen's experiments with *Poa* and many other experiments have shown, individual plants differ in the degree to which they respond to environmental changes. Although the change itself is not inherited, the capacity to respond phenotypically is under genetic control and can consequently be selected. Differences in the degree of response are a characteristic of whole populations and species. Their interpretation has interesting ramifications.

A population of plants whose offspring can grow equally well in many environments has a great survival and dispersal potential. Why, then, are all plants not highly variable and capable of growing in all kinds of environments? The answer to this question requires the accumulation of many more experimental data than are available at present, especially concerning the physiology of adaptation. Present theory states that there is probably a certain degree of incompatibility between the ability to utilize the resources of one environment in the most efficient way and the ability to utilize the resources of many environments. Furthermore, if this theory applies at any one place, natural selection will tend to select those plants that can make best use of the resources of the environment of that one place and produce the largest offspring in the face of competition from other plants.

Many plants will grow and reproduce outside their native area if they do not have to compete with other native plants. So, for example, Rollins (unpublished) transplanted plants of *Leavenworthia alabamica* and *L. crassa* from Alabama to Massachusetts, where they grew and reproduced naturally for five years, as long as other plants, particularly grasses, were removed from the plot. When, after five years, grasses were allowed to grow in the plot *Leavenworthia* plants were unable to compete and were eliminated by the grasses. It is clear that these species have the ability to withstand the rigors of the physical environment (climate and soil) of Massachusetts, but not to the extent of the native vegetation. When put into direct competition the introduced species loses out.

When offspring of wild species of normally cross-pollinated plants are grown in the greenhouse and, especially if the seed is obtained by self-pollinating the plants, a diverse array of phenotypes is usually produced. These are usually much more varied than those found growing naturally in the population. The conclusion is, therefore, almost inevitable: most populations of outbreeding plants can produce much more variability than that normally observed, or, in other words, the store of genetical variability is greater than that expressed in the population.

It is easy to understand the advantage of this stored variability for a population that is faced with an environment that changes generation after generation. If in each generation a population would produce only one kind of phenotype, the moment that type of organism is no longer capable of growing vigorously because of changes in the environment, and the death rate for that phenotype is higher than the birth rate, the population is in danger of extinction.

Every population has to have effective means of reproduction in order to survive generation after generation. This is usually referred to as immediate fitness. There is also an advantage in having the potential of producing off-spring that are different and possibly better equipped to deal with future changes in the environment. This is referred to as long-range flexibility.

The plant has no way of predicting what changes are going to occur, nor is it capable of "knowing" that changes are going to occur at all. Natural selection is for immediate fitness only. The phenotype and underlying geno-type that produce the largest offspring are selected and nothing else. Plants cope with the small yearly fluctuations in the weather and with minor topo-graphical differences in the environment largely by being phenotypically variable. Consequently, over a long period of time, a century for example, a certain phenotype and its underlying genotype will be favored. Most variants produced will be eliminated. This is the process of stabilizing selection already discussed in Chapter 2. But those variants are the insurance of the population for the time when the environment changes and selection changes from stabilizing to directional selection. How can mechanisms for storing this variability be selected? Probably they are not selected in the usual way, but rather are a necessary condition if a species is to survive over extensive periods of time. In other words, species that have no mechanism for storing genetical variability have a shorter life expectancy and should constitute a smaller proportion of any mature flora. If so, not all species should have mechanisms that store variability, and there should be a number of such mechanisms. The evidence is scanty as yet, but it does not seem to contradict these conclusions.

A detailed discussion of the different mechanisms that store variability will be given in Chapters 8 and 9. They are basically of three kinds: genic, chro-mosomal, and behavioral or mechanical. In diploid plants, genic systems are probably the most common and involve some kind of heterozygous superi-ority or genic dominance. Chromosomal mechanisms are those whereby the chromosomes behave in such a way that heterozygosity of some kind is maintained. Finally, behavioral or mechanical systems are those by which either the structure or the behavior of the flowers results in the formation of two kinds of seeds: some produced by self-pollinating and others produced by outcrossing.

In this chapter an attempt has been made to present the general picture of geographical variability in plant populations as it is understood and inter-preted today. Three important factors that play a role in producing and maintaining variability in populations have been omitted: hybridization, variation in the breeding systems, and the behavior of the chromosomes as carriers of the genes. These will be partly the subject matter of some of the next chapters.

Chapter 4

Breeding Systems

The manner of reproduction of a particular species is referred to as its breeding system. The breeding system is part of what Darlington (1939, 1958) has termed the *genetic system*. This latter term is defined as the totality of the hereditary mechanisms controlling variability and encompasses such matters as the number of chromosomes, the degree of crossing-over, the breeding system, and so on. Another useful concept is that of the recombination system (Carson, 1957). This term refers to the aspects of the genetic system controlling recombination. The breeding system is only one of the many factors regulating recombination in plants (Table 4–1). Basically, the breeding system can be either exclusively outbreeding (crossing always with another plant) or self-pollinating in various degrees.

TABLE 4–1

Classification of the Factors that Regulate Recombination in Plants. [Modified after Grant, 1958.]

I. Factors controlling the amount of recombination per unit of chronological time
   1. Length of generation

II. Factors controlling the amount of recombination per generation
   1. Chromosome number
   2. Frequency of crossing-over
   3. Postzygotic sterility barriers
   4. Breeding system
   5. Pollination system
   6. Dispersal potential
   7. Population size
   8. Crossability barriers and external isolating mechanisms

Mechanisms Controlling Self-incompatibility in Angiosperms

Charles Darwin, in his book *The Effect of Cross- and Self-Fertilization in the Vegetable Kingdom* (1888), describes the following experiments.

Ten flowers of plants of *Ipomea purpurea* ("Convolvulus major") were self-fertilized, and ten flowers from the same plant were fertilized with pollen from a different plant. Both kinds of pollination resulted in abundant seed set, and there was no significant difference in the number of seeds produced. The seeds resulting from these two kinds of pollination were then germinated and one of each kind planted on opposite sides of the same flower pot. Once the plants matured, they were measured. The results can be seen in Table 4–2.

TABLE 4–2

Average Plant Height and Seed Set per Capsule for Outbred and Inbred Plants of Ipomea purpurea. [Data from Darwin, 1888.]

	Outbred		Inbred	
Generation	Plant Height	Seeds/Capsule	Plant Height	Seeds/Capsule
1	86.0	5.23	65.5	4.85
2	84.1	—	66.3	—
3	77.41	4.73	52.8	4.43
4	69.8	4.75	60.1	4.47
5	82.5	3.37	62.3	3.00
6	87.5	—	63.2	—
7	83.9	—	68.3	—
8	113.6	—	96.7	—
9	81.3	—	64.0	—
10	93.7	—	50.4	—

The average height of the 6 outcrossed plants is 86 inches while that of the 6 self-fertilized plants is only 65.5 inches. More important, the first 5 plants resulting from cross-fertilization produced 121 seed capsules while those resulting from self-fertilization produced only 84 capsules. Of the 121 capsules on the crossed plants, 65 were the products of flowers crossed artificially with pollen from a different plant, and these contained an average 5.23 seeds per capsule. Of the 84 capsules on the self-fertilized plants, all the products of renewed self-fertilization, 55 were examined, and they contained an average 4.85 seeds per capsule. The crossed seeds were relatively heavier than the self-fertilized seeds (Darwin does not give any numerical values for this generation). Combining the number of capsules and the average number of seeds in each capsule, the crossed plants as compared with the self-fertilized ones yielded seeds in the ratio of 100 to 64, the first class being apparently heavier.

Darwin continued the experiment for ten generations, crossing the progeny of the line originally crossed and selfing that of the originally selfed. Generation after generation, the same advantage in height, number of capsules, number of seeds per capsule, and weight of the crossed over the self persisted, but increased in magnitude, so that by the end of the third generation the crossed plants produced seeds in comparison with the self-fertilized plants in a proportion of 100 to 35, the cross-fertilized seeds weighing 43.27 grains/100 seeds and the selfed 37.63/100 seeds.

Darwin repeated this kind of experiment with several dozen cultivated and wild plants, obtaining similar results in most cases. However, in certain cases the self-fertilized and the cross-fertilized plants showed no appreciable difference. One such case is *Mentzelia aurea* (*Bartonia aurea* in Darwin's account) in the Loasaceae. However, the plants did not grow well. Data only on plant height could be obtained and not on seed set. Another species in which the crossed plant did not show an advantage over the selfed one was the common pea, *Pisum sativum*, but Darwin suspected (and he was probably right) that he was dealing with genetically identical plants resulting from previous constant inbreeding, and that the comparison was not appropriate.

Darwin's conclusion from his experiments and observations was that, generally, cross-fertilization is beneficial and self-fertilization injurious. Studies and observations since that time have amply confirmed Darwin's insights. As a matter of fact, in many cases the pollen is incapable of germinating on the style of flowers of the plant that produced it or otherwise is incapable of fertilizing the egg, a condition referred to as *physiological* or *genetic self-incompatibility*. The converse condition, when the pollen can germinate on the style of flowers of the same plant and fertilize the egg, is called *self-compatibility*. Pollen of a self-compatible plant may habitually

TABLE 4-3

Incompatibility Mechanisms.

A. Control at the level of pollen germination and egg fertilization
  I. Multigenic systems: S type $\begin{cases}\text{sporophytically determined incompatibility}\\\text{gametophytically determined incompatibility}\end{cases}$
  II. Diallelic systems $\begin{cases}\text{with associated morphological differences (heterostyly)}\\\text{without associated morphological differences}\end{cases}$

B. Control in the timing of pollen maturity and availability of mature styles
  I. Protandry
  II. Protogyny

C. Control in the physical availability of receptive styles
  I. Unisexuality $\begin{cases}\text{monoecious-dicline}\\\text{dioecious}\\\text{polygamo-dioecious}\end{cases}$
  II. Architecture of the flower operating mechanically to impede selfing

fertilize the flower in which it was produced (self-pollinated) or it may habitually be prevented mechanically or otherwise from doing so.

In Table 4–3 the various types of incompatibility mechanisms that are found in plants have been listed. They will be discussed in more detail in what follows.

Multigenic Systems

By far the most common type of self-incompatibility is the multiple allelic kind found in each major phyletic line of the flowering plants, including over eighty angiosperm families as well as in some gymnosperms and ferns (East, 1940; Bateman, 1952; Fryxell, 1957). The inheritance of this type of self-sterility was first worked out by East and coworkers (East and Mangelsdorf, 1925; East, 1929) in the genus *Nicotiana*. In plants with this kind of self-sterility, plants fail to set seed when self-pollinated, although both eggs and pollen are fully fertile and produce abundant seed when the plant is crossed reciprocally with most other individuals of the population. Genetic analysis shows that each plant is heterozygous for a self-incompatibility factor S. In the population a series of alleles, indicated as $S^1, S^2, S^3, S^4 \cdots S^n$, are present ($n$ may be as high as 100). Normally the pollen tube will not grow in a style that carries the particular S allele present in the pollen grain itself. Thus, in the styles of a plant that is S^1/S^2, neither S^1 nor S^2 pollen grains grow well regardless of whether produced by the same plant or by another one, while a pollen grain with any other S allele grows perfectly well (Fig. 4–1).

Self-incompatible species possessing a multiple allelic incompatibility system can be divided into two groups: (1) the gametophytic type; and (2) the sporophytic type. In the gametophytic type each pollen grain expresses

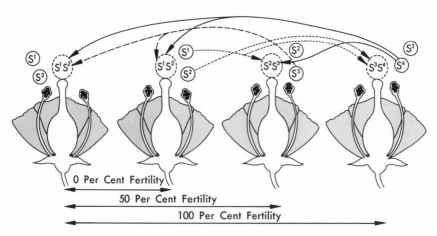

FIG. 4–1. Diagram showing the crossing relationships between self-incompatible plants. Unbroken circles show pollen grains; broken circles show genotypes of styles. (From Solbrig, 1966a.)

the incompatibility type of the S gene it carries whereas, in the sporophytic type, the pollen grain also expresses the incompatibility reaction of the S genes of the maternal plant. In other words, the genetic composition of the pollen alone determines the incompatibility reaction in the first kind, whereas the genetic composition of the tissues of the parent plants determines the incompatibility reaction in the second instance.

Knowledge regarding the cytological, physiological, and molecular aspects of self-incompatibility is still incomplete. Sporophytic types of self-incompatibility (see Table 4–4) are associated with trinucleate pollen and simul-

TABLE 4-4

Relationship Between Type of Incompatibility, Type of Pollen Mother Cell Division in Meiosis, and Number of Nuclei in Pollen Grains. [Adapted from Pandey, 1960.]

Flowers Homo-morphic or Heteromorphic	Type of Cytokinesis in Pollen Mother Cell	Number of Nuclei in Pollen Grains	System of Self-incom-patibility	Number of Families
Homomorphic	Both simultaneous and successive	2	Gametophytic	2
Homomorphic	Simultaneous	2	Gametophytic	28
Homomorphic	Successive	2	Gametophytic	5
Homomorphic	Successive*	3	Gametophytic	1
Homomorphic	Simultaneous*	3	Sporophytic	8
Heteromorphic	Simultaneous*	2	Sporophytic	5
Heteromorphic	Simultaneous	3	Sporophytic	4

* In some cases a family may have some species with simultaneous and others with successive cell division. The incompatibility depends in such cases on the particular kind of cytokinesis the species has, in accordance with the above table.

taneous formation of the cell walls at meiosis (after nuclear division), although species with heteromorphic (heterostylous) flowers have sporophytic incompatibility reactions and binucleate pollen. According to Pandey (1960), the sporophytic type of incompatibility is derived from the gametophytic type and functionally is related to an earlier time of action of the S allele so that all four products of meiosis receive the substance or substances that are involved in the incompatibility reaction. In the gametophytic type of incompatibility, gene action would not occur until the first cell wall after the first metaphase division of meiosis was formed and the substances produced by the S gene could not diffuse freely throughout the four cells (Fig. 4–2).

Heterostyly

The existence and the evolutionary role of heterostyly were shown first by Darwin in a series of articles between 1862 and 1868 and extended in his book *The Different Forms of Flowers on Plants of the Same Species* (1877).

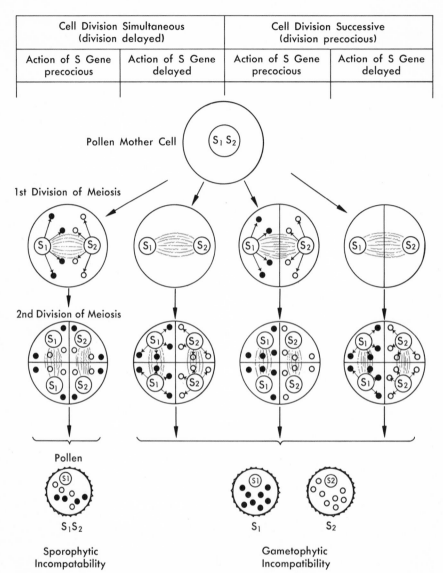

FIG. 4–2. Pandey's hypothesis (Pandey, 1960) to explain the correlation between cytological characteristics and type of incompatibility. According to this hypothesis, the incompatibility genes produce a substance (represented here by black and white dots) that controls the incompatibility reaction in the pollen grain. In the case where the action of the *S* gene is precocious (that is, it takes place before the onset of the second meiotic division) and cell division is retarded (taking place after the information of the four nuclei of the tetrad, the so-called simultaneous type), the substances of both genes are evenly distributed throughout the cytoplasm, and the pollen grain has a sporophytic type of incompatibility. In all other cases the incompatibility reaction is gametophytically determined.

Darwin noted that in the common garden primrose, *Primula vulgaris*, two kinds of flowers can be observed on different plants. One kind of flower has a long style and short stamens, the other has long stamens and a short style (Fig. 4–3). Darwin crossed the long-styled flowers (known as *pins*) with other long-styled flowers and also with short-styled flowers (known as *thrums*), and these last with other thrums as well. Invariably, crosses between thrums and pins yielded a large seed crop, while crosses between the same type of flower yielded little or no seed. It was clear that heterostyly was a means of preventing self-fertilization.

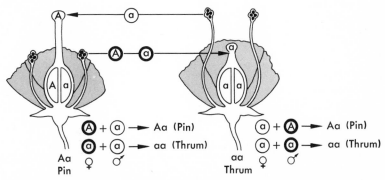

FIG. 4–3. Diagram of the crossing relationships between heterostylous (in this case distylous) plants. An *a* pollen produced by the pin plant reacts on the thrum style as if it were A. Note that both pin and thrum plants yield exactly one half pins and one half thrums in their progeny. (From Solbrig, 1966a.)

Heterostyly usually involves differences in length of the anther and style, sometimes two kinds such as in *Primula*, or less frequently three kinds as found in the genus *Oxalis*. Other morphological characters are often associated with heterostyly, particularly differences in pollen size and morphology and type of stigma hairs, but in some cases the morphological differences are minimal, as in some members of the Plumbaginaceae (Baker, 1948, 1953a).

However, it is not the morphological, but the genetic differences that are important. Lewis (1954) has shown that in the case of *Primula*, and probably other heterostylous species as well, the differences between the two incompatibility types can be traced to one complex locus, sometimes referred to as a *supergene*. Crossing-over within this complex locus is negligible, so that the complex is inherited as a block. Table 4–5 shows the genetic composition of the thrum and pin supergene of *Primula*. In the case of the primroses, the thrum is the heterozygous plant, *Ss*, and the pin the homozygous recessive, *ss*. This situation seems to be true in all cases studied except probably in certain members of the Plumbaginaceae, where the pin seems to be heterozygous

TABLE 4–5

Hypothetical Structure of the Supergene Controlling
Heterostyly in *Primula*. [After D. Lewis, 1954.]

Thrum	Pin
$\dfrac{GSI_1I_2PA}{gsi_1i_2pa}$	gsi_1i_2pa gsi_1i_2pa

I = stylar incompatibility
G = style length
S = stigma surface
A = anther height
I = pollen incompatibility
P = pollen size

(Baker, 1954). However, too few species have been investigated for definitive conclusions to be drawn.

The physiological incompatibility reaction of the style and pollen that prevents selfing is sporophytically determined in heterostylous plants. Styles and pollen of thrums with an *Ss* genetic composition behave as *S* and will respectively allow only germination of *s* pollen or will germinate only on *s* styles of the pins.

There is no consistency in the morphological and physiological expression of heterostyly in the different groups where it is found. The sporadic occurrence of heterostyly in different families and genera of angiosperms (Table 4–6) indicates that it has probably arisen independently several times during the evolution of the angiosperms. The evolution of heterostyly represents a case of convergent evolution. Therefore, although there is general agreement in the basic expression of the phenomenon, there are variations in detail. So, for example, some species, such as *Linum perenne*, have only a long style–short style morphological expression, whereas *L. grandiflorum* has dimorphism also in the stigma surface and pollen size. In the Plumbaginaceae a wide variety of combinations has been reported (Baker, 1948, 1953a). In *Narcissus*, polymorphic style length is believed to be associated with a multigenic incompatibility system (Dulberger, 1964). In *Amsinckia* (Ray and Chisaki, 1957), *Celosia*, *Chamissoa*, and *Heteranthera* (East, 1940), there is floral dimorphism, but apparently no associated physiological incompatibility.

Although it has been proposed (Crowe, 1964) that heterostyly arose directly from a homomorphic multigenic incompatibility system by loss of genes, heterostylous plants have most likely arisen from self-compatible plants (Vuilleumier, 1967). It is impossible to say if the physiological incompatibility arose first and was later reinforced by the morphological differences or if the converse is true, or, as is very likely, heterostyly has arisen via different mechanisms in different plant groups.

TABLE 4–6

Heterostylous Families. [Adapted from Vuilleumier, 1967.]

Family	Type of Heterostyly*
Polygonaceae	D
Capparaceae	D
Saxifragaceae	D
Connaraceae	D
Leguminosae	D
Oxalidaceae	D, T
Linaceae	D
Erythroxylaceae	D
Guttiferae	D
Turneraceae	D
Lythraceae	D, T
Primulaceae	D
Plumbaginaceae	D
Oleaceae	D
Loganiaceae	D
Gentianaceae	D
Polemoniaceae	D
Boraginaceae	D
Rubiaceae	D, T
Commelinaceae	D
Pontederiaceae	D, T
Iridaceae	D
Amaryllidaceae	D

* D = dimorphic; T = trimorphic

Other Diallelic Systems

Capsella bursa-pastoris (Riley, 1936), the shepherd's purse, possesses a diallelic incompatibility system. Only two genetical forms are found: the homozygous recessive *ss* and the heterozygous *Ss*. *S* pollen germinates normally only on *ss* styles, while *s* pollen germinates normally only on *Ss* styles. In this respect *Capsella bursa-pastoris* resembles heterostylous species. However, no morphological special characteristic of any kind has been associated with *Ss* or *ss* plants. This is so far the only nonheterostylous diallelic system known.

Protandry and Protogyny

Both these mechanisms involve the uneven maturation of the sex organs. A plant is said to be protandrous if at the time of the release of the pollen, the gynoecium is not yet developed to the point where fertilization of the ovules is possible. A plant is said to be protogynous, if at the time when the gynoecium is ready for the fertilization of the ovules, the pollen has not yet been released. Since blooming in a population is always staggered to a smaller or larger extent, in a protandrous species the styles will tend to be pollinated by the pollen of flowers that emerge a little later; the converse is true for protogynous species. However, the time gap between the maturation of pollen and style can be very short, so that some pollen is available for self-pollination towards the end of the time the flower stays open, provided that no previous cross-fertilization has taken place.

Protandry and protogyny are to be expected in species that are genetically self-compatible, and as such would be a mechanism to restore some degree of self-incompatibility to self-compatible species. Protandry and protogyny are known, however, also in species that are self-incompatible, as in many species of the family *Compositae*.

Unisexuality and Dioecism

In certain species of flowering plants the flowers are unisexual and of two types: those that produce only stamens and those that produce only carpels. If the two kinds of flowers are produced on the same plant, the individual is said to be monoecious, whereas in the cases in which the different kinds of flowers are produced on different individuals the plant is said to be dioecious. In other species, both bisexual and unisexual flowers are produced. In some cases, such as in the common European ash, *Fraxinus excelsior*, male, female, and hermaphrodite flowers are produced. Such a species is called polygamous: polygamodioecious if the different kinds of flowers are produced on different plants; polygamomonoecious if they are produced on the same plant. Still other species, such as *Plantago lanceolata*, have only two kinds of flowers: female and hermaphrodite flowers. Such species are known as gynodioecious plants, if the two kinds of flowers are associated with different plants, and gynomonoecious if on the same plant.

Unisexuality is another mechanism that prevents self-fertilization. Unisexuality is clearly derived in most angiosperms: most unisexual flowers have parts of the other sex in rudimentary form, such as in *Baccharis*. However, there are some species in which no rudiments of the other sex are present, such as in the willows. It is impossible to tell whether or not such species are primitively unisexual.

Because unisexuality in animals is usually determined by a pair of heteromorphic chromosomes (the XY or ZW systems), botanists have spent much effort searching for such systems in dioecious plants. The search has been quite fruitless in general. In most instances no differences have been found.

Nevertheless, in some thirteen families of angiosperms where the genetics of sex determination is fairly well understood (Westegaard, 1958), there are some species with true sex chromosomes. The genetic situation, however, is often more complex than that found in most animals (certain insects, particularly coccids, excluded). Two species that have been analyzed in detail are particularly fine examples. They are *Rumex hastatulus*, a dioecious dock of the southeastern United States, and *Melandrium album*, one of the campions in the pink family, a European plant that has spread to many parts of the world as a cultivated plant and as a roadside weed.

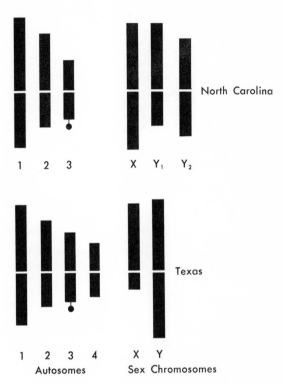

FIG. 4–4. Ideogram of the chromosomes of a male plant of *Rumex hastatulus* from North Carolina (above) with three autosomes, one X and two Y chromosomes; and Texas (below), with four autosomes, one X and one Y. (From B. Smith, 1964, by permission.)

Rumex hastatulus is a North American species of dock found in the Carolinas and south to Florida and west to Texas, Arkansas, and Missouri. Plants of populations from south and central Texas have ten chromosomes Female plants are homogametic, that is, they produce only one kind of gamete, which has four autosomes and one X chromosome. The males are heterogametic, that is, they produce two kinds of gametes, each with four autosomes and either one X chromosome or one Y chromosome. Populations from North Carolina, on the other hand, have only eight chromosomes. The females have six autosomes and two X chromosomes, whereas the males have six autosomes, one X and two Y (Y_1 and Y_2) chromosomes (Fig. 4-4). In addition, there are differences in the chromosome morphology (Smith, 1963, 1964). The origin and advantages of these two different karyotypes and sex-determining mechanisms are not entirely clear. Ben Smith (1964) has shown that the changes are due to a series of translocations (Fig. 4–5). He postulates

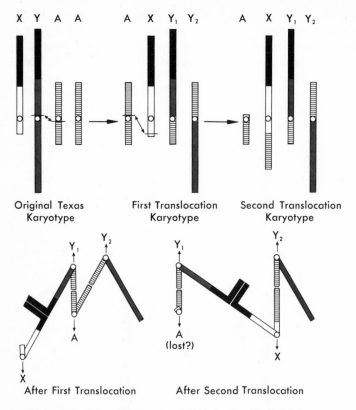

COORIENTATION OF SEX CHROMOSOMES AT MEIOSIS

FIG. 4–5. Hypothesis by which XY_1Y_2 sex chromosomes of *Rumex hastatulus* from North Carolina could have arisen by two successive translocations between the original XY chromosome pair of autosomes. White: differential region of the X; black: homologous segments of X and Y chromosomes; stippled: differential regions of the Y's; cross-hatched: segments of the original autosome. Points of assumed breakage and translocation are indicated by double-headed arrows. (From B. Smith, 1964, by permission.)

that the selective force favoring the change is the lower recombination index that a low chromosome number presumably gives. The evidence for this hypothesis is not very strong.

The situation in the campion *Melandrium album* does not involve changes in the karyotype, but in the proportion of the two sexes in the population. In a species with an XY chromosome sex-determining mechanism, such as in *Melandrium album*, approximately equal numbers of both sexes are expected in the population, because 50% of the pollen will produce male plants after fertilization and 50% will produce female plants. However, this is not the case in this species, in which there is always an excess of female plants. Correns (1928) established that the pollen grains that have an X chromosome grow faster on the style than pollen grains that have a Y chromosome. Consequently, when there is an excess of pollen on the style of the female plant, more X-chromosomed pollen fertilizes the ovules of the female plant (which are all X) than Y-chromosomed pollen, and as a result more female (XX) plants than male (XY) plants are produced in the next generation. However, as the proportion of females increases and males decreases in the population, there will be fewer pollen grains available to fertilize a greater number of ovules. In such a situation, the slower growing Y-chromosomed pollen will increasingly fertilize a larger number of ovules, and the proportion of male plants will again increase in the population. The system is a kind of self-regulating one that assures the production of the largest number of female plants and consequently of seeds, but at the same time keeps a sufficient supply of pollen available. Recently Mulcahy (1967) has reinvestigated the situation in detail as it occurs in natural populations, confirming the abnormal sex ratios. He also showed that male plants produce more flowers, contributing in this manner to a still more abnormal sex ratio (Table 4–7),

TABLE 4–7

Sex Ratios [Male Plants/Female Plants] and Average Flower Ratios [Male Flowers/Female Flowers] of Natural Populations of *Melandrium Album*. [From Mulcahy, 1967.]

Population	Sex Ratio	Average Flower Ratio
101 A	0.68	2.10
101 B + C	0.60	2.85
Szopa	0.32	6.00
Leavitt Hill	1.03*	4.90

* It was not possible to complete observations of this population. Since female plants flower later than male plants, the ratio is unnaturally high.

because a few male plants can fertilize a large number of female plants. Darlington (1958) had already suggested that a dioecious plant in which the staminate is the heterogametic sex, such as in *Melandrium album*, would adjust its sex ratio by selective pressures as outlined so that there would be more pistillate plants in the population than the 50% expected and so that the general population fitness would be increased. This is not possible when the female is the heterogametic sex and might explain why the male is the heterogametic sex in most species of dioecious plants even though apparently pistillate and staminate heterogamy can evolve with equal facility (Jones, 1932; Mulcahy, 1967). The same aberrant sex ratios as in *Melandrium album* have also been observed in *Rumex acetosa* (Correns, 1928) and in *Humulus japonicus* (Kihara and Hiroyashi, 1932), both of which possess staminate heterogamy, which further strengthens the hypothesis.

Outbreeding: Some Theoretical Considerations

The classical studies of Darwin reported in *The Effects of Self- and Cross-Fertilization in the Vegetable Kingdom* (1888) demonstrated that in many species that are usually outcrossed, selfing will result in a decreased seed set or no seed formation at all. This has been demonstrated repeatedly over the years, and examples were discussed at the beginning of this chapter.

Seedlings arising from self-pollinated seeds are often slow growing and less vigorous than those arising from cross-pollinated plants. Corn (*Zea mays*) illustrates the problem quite dramatically. Selfing the unisexual female flowers of the cob with the pollen of the tassel of the same plant results in progeny that is less vigorous than the parent and that sets fewer seeds. If this process is repeated for several generations, the inbreeding effect, called *inbreeding depression*, diminishes, until after five to ten generations no more of the effect is noticeable. The populations so obtained may be only one half or less the size of the parental outbreeding populations, and their seed set (used usually as the measure of fitness) is only a fraction of that of the parental line. If two such lines are then intercrossed, the resulting offspring is more vigorous and has a higher seed set than either of the outcrossing parents used to produce the inbred lines. This *hybrid vigor* or *heterosis*, as this effect is called, can sometimes be very striking as for example in corn. Not all outbreeding plants show these effects as dramatically as corn, and even in corn some lines show stronger inbreeding depression and more hybrid vigor than others.

The reasons why selfing should result in a lowered seed set and in less vigorous offspring are not completely understood. This area is one of active research, because this information is very important to the formulation of the best programs for improving crops by plant breeding.

When plants are inbred, most heterozygous loci will become homozygous, following Mendel's second genetic law, which stipulates that half of the offspring is homozygous. If the outbreeding line possesses recessive semilethals or deleterious genes, they will become expressed in the inbred lines, leading to a reduced vigor. When two lines are then crossed, the original heterozygous condition is restored. The increased vigor may be due to the fact that more genes will be in a heterozygous state in the hybrid than in the original outcrossed lines, where a number may have been homozygous recessives to start with. This theory explains hybrid vigor by a so-called additive effect of the dominant loci. The number of lethals and other deleterious genes in the population is called the *genetic load* of the population (Dobzhansky and Spassky, 1963).

Why, we may ask, do so many deleterious genes persist in the population?

In a population exposed to natural selection, deleterious genes should be selected against unless they confer some advantage. One explanation is that deleterious genes may persist in the population because they are deleterious only when homozygous, but are advantageous when heterozygous. There is some evidence that this may be the case in certain species of plants and animals. In barley (*Hordeum sativum*), the hybrid between two lines differing in only one gene is more vigorous than either parent (Hagberg, 1953). If it were simply a case of masking a recessive gene, the hybrid should not be more vigorous than the parent with the dominant gene. Obviously the combination of the two alleles is better than either of the genes in double doses. This situation is called *overdominance* or *single gene heterosis*.

The biochemical basis of single gene heterosis has been worked out in many cases. One of them is in the bread mold *Neurospora crassa*. The nuclei in this fungus are haploid, but two can exist in the same cytoplasm to form a so-called *heterokaryon*, in which the cells are binucleate. A heterokaryon is genetically and physiologically equivalent to a diploid. One such heterokaryon grew better than either of the two parents, which differed by a single gene (Emerson, 1952). It turned out that the allele present in one parent produced too little para-aminobenzoic acid, a vitamin needed for growth. The other allele present in the second parent produced too much of the same vitamin; the combination of the two genes in the heterokaryon produced an amount optimal for growth.

There is still another explanation for hybrid vigor or heterosis. This is the so-called *epistatic* effect of genes. It is well known that genes do not affect a single characteristic of the phenotype but many, although the main effect may be quite localized. This multiple effect of a gene is due to the fact that the primary gene products, the enzymes, catalyze a specific chemical reaction in the metabolism of the cell, and consequently all cells in which the particular reaction takes place will be affected by the gene. Two independent genes may affect the same metabolic pathway. When they do, the rate and timing of gene action in one gene has to be in phase with the rate and timing of gene action of the second gene. If they are not, all kinds of interferences are theoretically possible.

In a strict sense, an epistatic interaction exists when one gene masks the effect of another so that the phenotype is determined by the former gene and not by the latter when both genes are present in the same genotype. The gene that thus masks or prevents the expression of another is said to be epistatic to it, and the gene that is hidden is said to be hypostatic. An example is the inheritance of fruit color in summer squash. The gene for white (*WW*) is nonallelic and epistatic to those for yellow (*YY*) and green (*yy*), so that when the white gene is present in the dominant form (*WW*, *Ww*), no color is formed (Sinnot and Durham, 1922). Although the biochemistry is not known, the gene for white obviously must block some step in the metabolic pathway that leads to color.

The term *epistatic* is also used in a broader context to denote any kind of nonallelic interaction and not only a masking or inhibitory effect. It is especially used to denote a contribution to fitness by two or more nonallelic genes that is greater than the sum of the absolute value of their separate effects. For example, there is evidence (Sehgal, 1963) that certain segments of corn grass (*Tripsacum*) chromosomes when introduced into a corn (*Zea*) background produce hybrid vigor because of their interaction with corn genes. Thus, nonallelic epistatic interactions in diploids may be an added cause of heterosis.

Not all species are heterotic although many show inbreeding depression. However, in addition to heterotic effects on fitness there are other selective advantages that a population can derive from a heterozygosity maintained by outbreeding. Foremost is the basic fact that the potential genetic variability of a population will be increased. In effect, a population homozygous for the gene A_1A_1 will have only one phenotype; a population that has two alleles, A_1A_2, has the potential of forming three genotypes; one with three alleles, $A_1A_2A_3$, has the potential of forming six genotypes

$$(A_1A_1; A_1A_2; A_1A_3; A_2A_2; A_2A_3; A_3A_3),$$

and so on, according to the general formula $g_A = r(r + 1)/2$ (see page 21).

In brief, outbreeding is favored because it increases heterozygosity. In turn, heterozygosity is beneficial in general terms because it usually increases the potential variability of the population, produces heterosis, and leads to a more developmentally stable population. The theoretical reasons as well as the experimental evidence are still being developed, and these conclusions are in part still tentative.

The Establishment of Inbreeding

If heterozygosity is so important, how is it possible that some very successful species are inbreeders and consequently (at least in theory) homozygous? This is one of the most fascinating areas of study in biosystematics, one for which the answers are not yet all in.

It is generally accepted that self-incompatibility is the primitive condition in most taxa and that probably self-compatibility is always derived in the flowering plants. The main lines of evidence that point to this conclusion are four (Stebbins, 1957):

1. In those genera where the phylogeny is fairly well understood, the self-fertilizing species clearly appear to be more specialized in morphological characteristics than many of their self-incompatible and cross-fertilizing relatives. A very good example is the situation found in the genus *Leavenworthia* (Rollins, 1963; Lloyd, 1965), where the self-compatible species are

all highly specialized and derived from self-incompatible ones (Fig. 4–7, page 68).

2. Many self-fertilizing species possess structures that could be of use only in connection with cross-fertilization, such as the colorful papilionate flowers of the Leguminosae-Papilionoideae, still present in many self-fertilizing species of the family, such as the lima bean (*Phaseolus lunatus*).

3. Genetic studies (D. Lewis, 1954, 1955; Pandey, 1960) have shown that different genera of the same family or of closely related families have similar genetic bases for incompatibility pointing to a common origin.

4. Finally, self-fertilizing species or populations have been observed to originate in historical times from self-incompatible ones in several lines, as in the case of the cultivated snapdragon, *Antirrhinum majus*, the only self-fertilizing species in an otherwise self-incompatible genus.

Furthermore, genetic studies have shown that the change from multigenic self-incompatibility to self-compatibility is relatively simple, whereas the converse requires the accumulation of a series of apparently rarely occurring genetic events. It is, therefore, assumed that the multigenic self-incompatibility systems of the angiosperms have originated only a very few times during the course of evolution, probably early in the evolution of the angiosperms, if indeed these systems do not antecede the emergence of the group.

But not all incompatibility is of the multigenic type, and there is indirect evidence that in some species a multigenic type has given rise to self-compatible species that in turn have given rise to self-incompatible species with different mechanisms of self-incompatibility, such as heterostyly or dioeciousness. Consequently, in some cases at least, self-incompatibility may be the derived condition.

A plant, in order to outcross with another one, requires the aid of an outside agent to carry the pollen or the gametes from one plant to another. This outside agent is water for the nonvascular plants as well as for the ferns and fern-allies and for a few angiosperms. The agent is wind for practically all of the gymnosperms (apparently insects aid in the pollination of some cycads and gnetales) and many flowering plants, such as many northern hemisphere trees (oaks, maples, birches, poplars, elms), as well as grasses, sedges, ragweeds, and so on. But most flowering plants (including most of the plants with showy flowers such as members of the Leguminosae, Cruciferae, Orchidaceae, Compositae, Scrophulariaceae, Labiatae, Cactaceae, and so on) are pollinated by flying insects, particularly beetles, flies, bees, wasps, and butterflies. Finally, a few specialized species have other pollinating agents, such as ants (e.g., Bullhorn acacias), bats, birds, and even frogs.

Cross-pollination by water and wind is a mechanical phenomenon. It requires a mechanism that allows for the release of the pollen into the water or air and pollen grains that will float in the water or air. Wind pollination is most effective in areas where there is a reasonable amount of air flow and little physical interference, such as in the prairies or in a northern deciduous forest in the springtime before the leaves are out. The wind and water will carry the gametes (or gametophytes) passively. Many gametes are consequently wasted when they land on the wrong tree or on rocks, stems, foliage, and so on. Plants that rely on wind pollination produce large amounts of pollen to compensate for this waste.

Animals are in general more effective as pollinating agents than wind or water. They are attracted in their visits to flowers by the prospect of food in the form of nectar or pollen (and occasionally other structures). After feeding on one flower they will usually visit another one, often of the same species, and carry on their bodies pollen from the first flower, with which they unknowingly pollinate the flowers. Flowers of the plants that rely on animals for their pollination attract the animals with their bright colors, special forms, and lure of food (Baker, 1963; Solbrig, 1966). Because animals are more efficient than wind or water, animal-pollinated flowers usually produce less pollen. Many flowers have developed a series of very excellent, fine adaptations for attracting certain insects and excluding others in order to assure cross-fertilization with maximum efficiency.

However, there are ecological situations in which pollinating agents are absent. In cold areas insects do not appear until the weather has warmed up; in tropical areas there are more obstacles to efficient movement of pollen by air; in desert areas there is no water. In these situations plants that depend for their fertilization on the missing pollinating agent are excluded, unless they revert to self-pollination.

The situation in the genus *Leavenworthia* is a very fine example of reversion to self-pollination. This is a small and distinctive genus of the family Cruciferae that grows in Alabama, Tennessee, Missouri, and adjacent areas. It shows an unusually close adaptation for growth in areas known as cedar glades. These cedar glades exhibit a combination of shallow soil depth and thinly bedded dolomitic limestone that maintains a temporarily high moisture content at or very near the surface during the wet winter months. The limestone is covered with only a few inches of soil or may be completely barren in some spots (Rollins, 1963; Quarterman, 1950). Such open glades are extremely wet in the winter and spring, but very dry in the summer months. They are found primarily in central Tennessee, but also in Alabama, Kentucky, Missouri (especially in the Ozarks), and a few sites in Texas, Indiana, and Ohio.

Of the eleven species found in the genus, three, *Leavenworthia alabamica*, *L. stylosa*, and *L. crassa*, are primarily self-incompatible; all the others are self-compatible. The change in breeding system has been accompanied by a series of morphological changes to assure self-pollination (Figs. 4–6 and 4–7). So, for example, in the self-compatible species the flowers have become smaller, the styles shorter so that they are level with the anthers, and the anthers now open to the inside (toward the style), rather than outward.

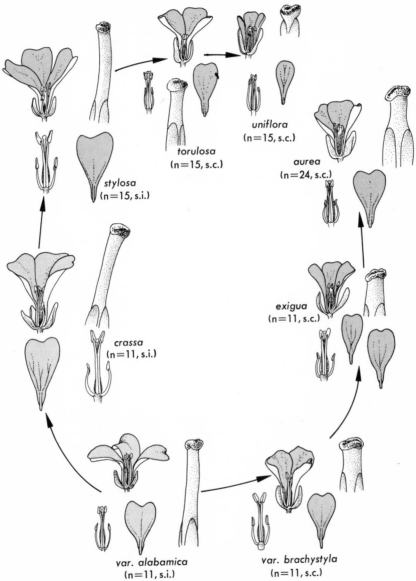

FIG. 4–6. Flower, stigma, stamens, and petals of species of *Leavenworthia* arranged in their probable evolutionary sequence, starting with *L. alabamica*. Note how the flowers become smaller, the styles become shorter, but not the stigmas, and how the stamens tend to grow appressed to the styles, with increasing self-compatibility. Flowers and petals two times natural size, stamens three times, styles, ten times. (From Rollins, 1963.)

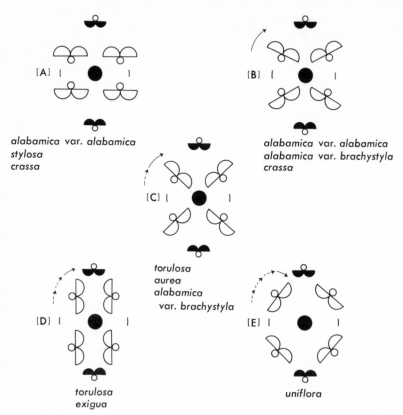

[A]

alabamica var. *alabamica*
stylosa
crassa

[B]

alabamica var. *alabamica*
alabamica var. *brachystyla*
crassa

[C]

torulosa
aurea
alabamica
    var. *brachystyla*

[D]

torulosa
exigua

[E]

uniflora

FIG. 4–7.   Diagrams of stamen patterns with respect to stigma in species of *Leavenworthia*. The stigma at center is represented by a black dot. The dehiscence lines of the anthers are on the rounded portion of each anther sac. Note how in the course of evolution with the change from self-incompatibility to self-compatibility, the anthers have changed from dehiscing away from the stigma to dehiscing toward the stigma. (From Rollins, 1963.)

These changes vary in degree of their completion in the various species. They culminate in the species *L. uniflora*, a species in which the flowers hardly open and most flowers are self-fertilized. What has brought this change about? Rollins (1963) and Lloyd (1965), after detailed studies, arrived at the conclusion that a lack of pollinators in early spring favored self-compatible plants. They showed that as a consequence of the long climatic trend of increasing aridity present in the central basin of Tennessee, the glades were drying out in the spring before insects had emerged in sufficient quantities to cross-fertilize the plants of *Leavenworthia*. This was most pronounced in the northern areas of Tennessee and Missouri where only self-compatible species were found, but not so much in Alabama, where the two self-incompatible species of the genus grew.

Another classical example, in this case of a whole flora, was demonstrated by Hagerup(1950, 1951) in the Faeroe Islands where it rains almost constantly. Many species with bright flowers that are insect-pollinated on the mainland, such as *Narthecium ossifragum*, are self-pollinated in the Faeroe Islands, raindrops carrying the pollen from the anthers to the stigma.

Advantages of Self-compatibility

Once a species has shifted from self-incompatibility to self-compatibility, it gains certain advantages and characteristics associated with self-pollination. One direct advantage is that single seeds that are carried away from the original population can reproduce and form a new population by themselves. In outbreeding species, two plants within pollinating distance are required for either to set seed. As has been pointed out by Baker (1953b, 1955), this characteristic of self-pollinating species facilitates, if it does not directly foster, establishment after long-range dispersal (if the probability of a seed being carried from one locality to another favorable locality over a stretch of unfavorable territory is 10^{-2} [1%], the probability of two seeds of different plants being carried more or less simultaneously is 10^{-4} [0.01%]). Many examples have been offered to substantiate "Baker's rule." One given by Baker (1948, 1953) is taken from the family Plumbaginaceae. The genera *Limonium* and *Armeria* have a number of species with heterostylous dimorphic flowers in Eurasia, while the species growing in America, which have presumably gotten there by long-range dispersal, are monomorphic and self-compatible.

Stebbins (1950, 1957) has advanced the hypothesis that species that occupy temporary habitats also derive a direct advantage from self-fertilization in that they can build up large populations from one invader whenever such a habitat is open. Many of our common weeds are self-compatible and self-pollinating. Baker's rule and "Stebbins' corollary" explain in part why these weeds are so widespread.

Self-compatible species should be more homozygous than self-incompatible species. How much more is an open question that several workers are trying to answer (Allard, 1965; Jain and Marshall, 1967; Carson, 1967). Theoretically, in each generation of a selfer the number of homozygous loci in a population doubles. Consequently, in only ten generations the homozygous loci should increase a thousandfold, making each plant in the population virtually homozygous. Different individuals will have different alleles, but in most plants they should be in a homozygous condition.

However, there are two major factors that can modify this scheme. Although all flowers in the population are self-compatible, not all plants in each generation are self-pollinated. The amount of outbreeding varies from species to species. In wheat (*Triticum* spp.) it is less than 1%; in barley (*Hordeum sativum*) about 1%; in the lima bean (*Phaseolus lunatus*) and in pigweeds

(*Amaranthus* spp.) about 5%. The progeny of these few outbreeding plants will be heterozygous for a number of loci.

But even 5% of outbreeding in each generation would, by itself, maintain only a small degree of heterozygosity in the population. It is the second controlling factor, namely *hybrid superiority*, that can modify this degree drastically. By hybrid superiority is meant that the outbreeding plant sets a larger number of seeds.

In a competition experiment between four homozygous varieties of barley, Suneson (1949) showed (Fig. 4–8) that one of them (Atlas) soon outcompeted the other three. In his experiment occasional intervarietal hybrids that were formed were removed. In a similar experiment with lima beans done by Allard (1965) the hybrids that were formed were allowed to remain in order to create a situation closer to what occurs in natural populations. Within six generations the two original pure lines were swamped by a hybrid swarm even though outcrossing was less than 5%. The experiment points to a definite hybrid advantage, because the increase of the hybrids cannot be explained on the basis of outbreeding alone (Fig. 4–9).

Some outbreeding and hybrid advantage can consequently keep a population of an inbreeding species from becoming completely homozygous. Allard and Hansche (1965) have calculated the amount of heterozygosity that could exist in a population of inbreeders with 5% outcrossing and different values of hybrid superiority. Given a mean fitness of $s = 0.6$ for the homozygous and $s = 1$ for the heterozygous, the population would attain 80% of the heterozygosity (under the conditions of the calculation) that it could attain

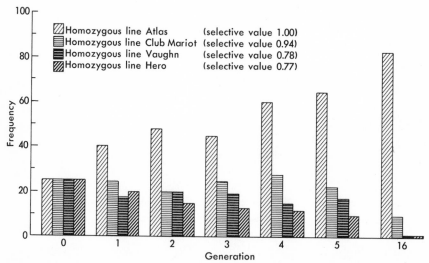

FIG. 4–8. Effect of natural selection on a mixture of homozygous lines of barley. Hybrids were removed. One line, Atlas, out-competed the others. (Data from Suneson, 1949.)

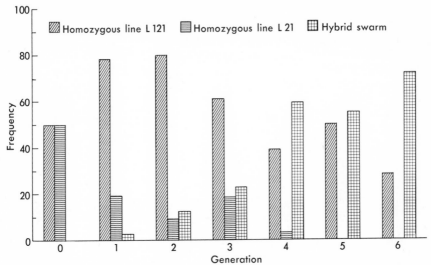

FIG. 4–9. Effect of natural selection on a mixture of homozygous lines of lima bean, where hybrids were allowed to reproduce. One line, L121, soon outcompeted the other, but after a few generations the hybrid out-competed both. Compare with the barley experiment, Fig. 4–8. (Redrawn from Allard, 1965, by permission.)

if it were totally outbreeding. With an $s = 0.98$ for the homozygote and $s = 1.0$ for the heterozygote, that is, only a 2% advantage for the heterozygous over the homozygous, 25% of the theoretically maximum is still attained. Autogamous species need not be completely homozygous!

However, in some species a large degree of homozygosity is apparently present. Why this is so in some and not in others depends on many factors, not all of them as yet well understood. Random genetic drift and Mayr's founder principle (see Chapter 2) may be major reasons. In effect, whenever the size of the population is very much reduced by random phenomena or whenever a new population is started from one or a very few seeds, the total variability in the population is very low. In such cases recombination cannot increase this variability, only mutation and gene flow from neighboring populations can.

Recently Jain and Marshall (1967) made a comparative study of the variability of two species of wild oats, *Avena fatua* and *A. barbata*. They found that for a number of marker genes *A. barbata* was largely monomorphic while *A. fatua* was polymorphic. In other words, in the first case only one allele for the loci studied was present in each population while in the second there were at least two (Fig. 4–10). They also showed that in populations of *A. fatua* there was definite hybrid advantage. Jain and Marshall also obtained values for the degree of morphological variability in the populations (Table

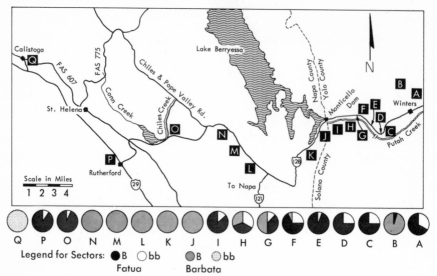

FIG. 4–10. Map showing localities where populations of wild oats, *Avena fatua* and *A. barbata*, were sampled by Jain and Marshall in California. Shown at the bottom are pie-shaped diagrams giving the proportion of black and gray lemmas, a character determined by a single gene. Note that in any given population plants of *A. barbata* are either black or gray, whereas plants with black and gray lemmas of *A. fatua* coexist in the same population. This last situation is probably an indication that in *A. fatua* there are more heterozygous plants (because of hybrid superiority?) and consequently some gray genotypes (*bb*) are always segregating. (From Jain and Marshall, 1967, by permission.)

4–8). It was found that *A. barbata*, although apparently more homozygous genetically, was more variable because of a larger nongenetic component, that is, it was more plastic.

Here then are two very closely related species growing in the same habitat with similar requirements that nevertheless possess two different genetic systems for dealing with the vagaries of the environment. One, *A. fatua*, is genetically polymorphic and can produce many kinds of genotypes, some of

TABLE 4–8

Comparison of Family Means for Three Characters in Two Species of *Avena* at Two Different Sites. [Data from Jain and Marshall, 1967.]

	Locality H		Locality A	
Character	*A. fatua*	*A. barbata*	*A. fatua*	*A. barbata*
Seed size	1.16–1.65	1.13–1.62	1.18–1.49	1.09–1.50
No. of spikelets	32.3–80.4	53.1–77.3	39.1–73.0	33.0–81.1
Panicle length	18.6–32.4	27.1–32.8	21.9–29.0	22.3–33.4

which presumably can grow in almost every environmental situation. The other, *A. barbata*, on the other hand, is genetically uniform, but very plastic, and it adapts phenotypically to the various situations.

In conclusion, it is very clear that self-compatible plants can adopt different strategies to overcome the disadvantages of homozygosity while still gaining the advantages of self-pollination. The degree of environmental fluctuation, the availability of pollinators, the amount of phenotypic plasticity are a few of the factors that will determine the strategy selected for the species to survive. And in turn these strategies determine the structure of the populations and the nature of the morphological variability and of the diversity among taxa that lie at the very heart of the systematist's interest. This is an area that the biosystematist should never neglect to investigate, because without an adequate knowledge of the breeding behavior no understanding of the properties of a species is possible.

Chapter 5

Speciation

One of the most intricate problems in biosystematics is the definition and delimitation of the species. Basically, the difficulty stems from the existence of two facets to the species problem. One of these is the delimitation of the evolutionary unit; the other is the taxonomic problem of concretely identifying a specific set of individuals as belonging to a particular species. Let us consider the problem first from the biological point of view, concentrating specifically on the processes that lead to the formation of species, leaving for later the discussion on how species can be defined for taxonomic purposes.

The Concept of the Species

Broad application of a useful and workable system of nomenclature and a system of classification during the last century brought into focus the problem of the nature of the basic unit that was being classified, namely, the species. In logical terms the species is a class to which belong all the objects that have certain common properties. The question, then, is what are the properties that define species and what are the biological processes underlying their existence? According to the dicta that have been traditionally used in plant taxonomy, the properties used to define a species are characteristics of the phenotype usually, but not necessarily always, pertaining to the exterior morphology. However, a species is not defined by only one character; there must be a series of correlated characters. This way of defining the species has been called the morphological species concept. The number and kind of characters by which a morphological species is defined varies widely according to the groups of plants being classified, but it is an undeniable fact that most plants can be grouped into species on the basis of a series of correlated morphological characters alone.

Evolutionary theory brought into focus the genetic relationships between members of a breeding population as well as their genetic continuity through time. This led to a redefinition of the species in genetic terms, a definition that has often been called the *biological species concept*, first introduced by Dobzhansky (1937) and later redefined and amplified by Mayr (1942, 1947, 1957, 1963): "Species are groups of actually or potentially interbreeding natural populations, which are reproductively isolated from other such groups." According to the biological species concept, species are classified by only one criterion, reproductive isolation.

A first question that emerges from the redefinition of the species is the correlation between the species defined in terms of morphology and in terms of reproductive isolation.

Correlation Between Morphology and Reproductive Isolation

Most, if not all, species of plants that are not related, such as species belonging to different families, are morphologically distinct and genetically isolated. Most, but not all, species that are related, that is, those belonging to the same genus, are morphologically distinct and reproductively (but not necessarily genetically!) isolated. Good examples are furnished by the genus *Glandularia*.

This genus, often also considered as section *Glandularia* of the genus *Verbena*, is widespread in South America, where it grows from Perú to Argentina, and in North America, where it is found from Guatemala to the central and eastern United States. Species of *Glandularia* are easily distinguished from species of the closely related genus *Verbena* and repeatedly, when crosses between species of the two genera were attempted, no seed was produced. However, crosses between most of the species of *Glandularia* can be produced. Their fertility and their natural occurrence are of interest to this discussion.

Let us consider the three South American species, *G. peruviana*, *G. pulchella*, and *G. santiaguensis*. These three species occupy approximately the same habitat: open, dry, and semidry grassland in northern and central Argentina. *Glandularia pulchella* and *G. santiaguensis* replace each other geographically, with the former growing in the cooler southern and eastern areas and the latter in the more subtropical northern and western areas. *Glandularia peruviana* stretches over all of the territory occupied by the other two species. Morphologically, *G. peruviana* differs from the other species because of its entire leaves, a more appressed habit, larger internodes, large red flowers, and absence of glandular appendages. *Glandularia santiaguensis* in turn is larger than *G. pulchella*, with large leaves and flowers and less divided leaves (Fig. 5–1). Natural hybrids between these three species are occasionally seen in the field, but they are rare. When they were obtained artificially in the experimental garden they were approximately 40–50% pollen fertile, and only about 1% of the flowers set seeds. It can then be seen that the genetic isolating barrier among the three species is about the same and that the species are almost absolutely reproductively isolated.

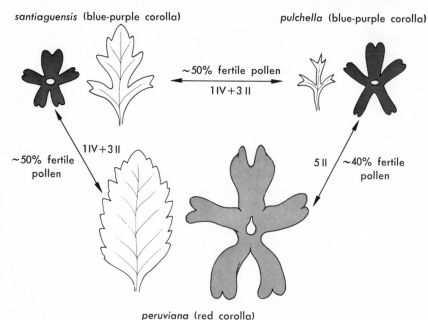

FIG. 5–1. Leaf shape and corolla of three species of *Glandularia*, and the pollen fertility and chromosome pairing relationships of the hybrids among them. Note that although *G. peruviana* is morphologically less similar to *G. santiaguensis* and *G. pulchella* than these two are to each other, the hybrids between all three species are approximately equal in pollen fertility. As to chromosome architecture, *G. santiaguensis* is more dissimilar to the other two species than they are to each other. These three species illustrate the reticulate nature of evolution.

Crosses between *G. peruviana* and two other morphologically distinct species, *G. megapotamica* and *G. moricolor*, on the other hand, yielded hybrids that were more fertile. The cross between *G. peruviana* and *G. megapotamica*, for example, was approximately 65% pollen fertile and the cross between *G. peruviana* and *G. moricolor* was approximately 80% pollen fertile. Morphologically, *G. megapotamica* is similar to *G. peruviana* although it has flowers of a different color and is more erect. *Glandularia moricolor*, on the other hand, is quite distinct, having elliptic leaves, erect habit, smaller and deep purple flowers, and a more compact inflorescence. Neither of these two species grows together with *G. peruviana*. *Glandularia megapotamica* grows in the subtropical gallery forest of northeastern Argentina, Brazil, and Paraguay, whereas *G. moricolor* is a species of the margins of the subtropical forest of northern Argentina. Consequently, the genetic isolation between these two species and *G. peruviana* is not complete. However, they are effectively isolated reproductively because they do not grow together. Reproductive isolation is not necessarily genetic isolation.

However, the correlation between morphological differences and reproductive isolation is not universal. For example, a lack of reproductive isolation is found among many species of oaks and other kinds of trees. In a now classical study, C. H. Muller (1952) studied a series of four species of oaks in Texas. He found that they hybridize readily and that apparently their hybrids are perfectly fertile. However, each of the four species is adapted to a different type of soil: *Quercus mohriana* to limestone, *Q. havardi* to sand, *Q. grisea* to igneous outcrops, and *Q. stellata* to clay. Hybrids are able to grow only in areas where the various soil types overlap. Since these hybrid soil conditions are relatively rare, the hybrids are less abundant than the parents. These morphological oak species are neither genetically nor reproductively isolated. However, their hybrids are unadapted to the existing edaphic conditions and cannot become established. The pattern of morphologically distinct species that grow within pollination range of each other and that are not reproductively isolated but are ecologically specialized is relatively common among related species of long-lived woody plants. Other known examples are *Salvia mellifera–Salvia apiana* (Epling, 1947a; Grant and Grant, 1964, see page 99), certain species of *Betula* and *Populus* (Barnes 1961 and unpublished), and *Arctostaphylos* (Gottlieb, 1968).

Turning to annual species, still another kind of noncorrelation between morphological difference and reproductive isolation is found, namely that of genetically isolated populations that are morphologically identical or very similar. One such case that has been thoroughly investigated is the *Gilia inconspicua* complex of species studied by Grant (1964a). This complex ranges throughout the arid regions of western North America and southern South America where the plants occur in open sandy places in a variety of habitats. They can be found growing in desert washes or sandy river floodplains, in openings of the desert-scrub vegetation, or on the slopes of mountains. The individuals are self-compatible, and the pollen is deposited on the stigma lobes automatically. The products of self-pollination are fully vigorous generation after generation, as was shown by Grant (1964a) in experimental progenies. At maturity the plants belonging to the *Gilia inconspicua* complex bear small, dull-colored flowers on the upper branches. Although alike in their general characteristics, they also differ in various fine details of external morphology. On the basis of detailed morphological, cytological, and crossing experiments, it was possible to demonstrate that what had been considered one species was actually a group of six independently derived groups of species, comprising no less than twenty-five species altogether (Table 5–1 and Fig. 5–2). With very few exceptions, all twenty-five of these species are completely genetically isolated from each other, no hybrid seed having been formed in spite of repeated attempts at crossing. In the few cases where hybrids were produced, they were very sterile (highest fertility, 28% of fertile pollen). The pattern found in these species of *Gilia* is known from other groups of annuals, such as certain species of *Clarkia* (Lewis, 1962), *Oenothera* (Raven,

TABLE 5–1

Synoptical List of Small-Flowered Cobwebby Gilias Grouped According to Their Morphological and Cytogenetic Relationships into More or Less Natural Species Groups. [From Grant, 1964, by Permission of Author and Publisher.] See Also Fig. 5–2.

A. Gilia ochroleuca Group (Diploids)
1. *Gilia ochroleuca ochroleuca* Jones. Mojave Desert, California
2. *Gilia "obispo."* South Coast Ranges and San Diego Co., California
3. *Gilia mexicana* A. Grant and V. Grant. Desert grassland; Arizona, New Mexico, and northern Chihuahua, with a disjunct area in northern Baja California
4. *Gilia clokeyi* Mason. E. California to NW New Mexico
5. *Gilia "bradbury."* Death Valley, California
6. *Gilia aliquanta* A. Grant and V. Grant. Mojave Desert, California, and SW Nevada

B. Gilia tenuiflora Group (Diploids)
7. *Gilia interior* (Mason and A. Grant) A. Grant. California and Nevada
8. *Gilia austrooccidentalis* A. Grant and V. Grant. Inner South Coast Ranges, California
9. *Gilia jacens* A. Grant and V. Grant. Inner South Coast Ranges, California
10. *Gilia minor* A. Grant and V. Grant. Central California to W. Arizona
11. *Gilia salticola* Eastwood. Eastern Sierra Nevada and western Great Basin, California and Nevada.

C. Gilia brecciarum Group (Diploids)
12. *Gilia brecciarum brecciarum* Jones. Oregon and Nevada to southern California
13. *Gilia diegensis* (Munz) A. Grant and V. Grant. Southern California

D. Gilia inconspicua Group proper (Tetraploids)
14. *Gilia tweedyi* Rydberg. Oregon to Wyoming
15. *Gilia inconspicua* (Smith) Sweet. Washington to northern Nevada and Utah
16. *Gilia transmontana* (Mason and A. Grant) A. Grant and V. Grant. Mojave Desert, California to western Utah
17. *Gilia malior* A. Day and V. Grant. California and Nevada
18. *Gilia flavocinta australis* (A. Grant and V. Grant) A. Day and V. Grant. Arizona and New Mexico
19. *Gilia ophtalmoides* Brand. Eastern California to Colorado and New Mexico

E. Gilia sinuata Group (Tetraploids)
20. *Gilia sinuata I* (*G. sinuata* Douglas). Washington to western Colorado and southern California
21. *Gilia sinuata II.* Arizona
22. *Gilia modocensis* Eastwood. Eastern Oregon through Nevada and southern California
23. *Gilia tetrabreccia* A. Grant and V. Grant. South-central California

F. Gilia crassifolia Group (Tetraploids and Octoploids)
24. *Gilia crassifolia 4* ×. Argentina and probably Chile
25. *Gilia crassifolia 8* ×. Southern Argentina (Patagonia)

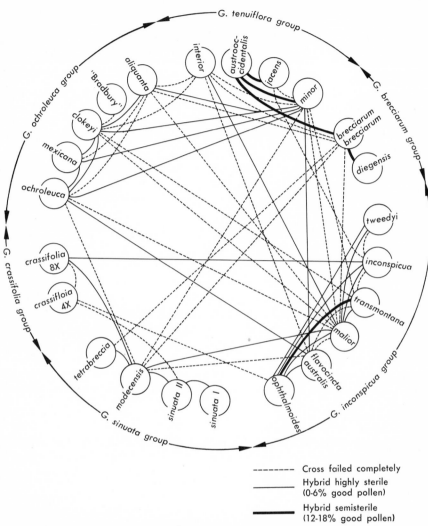

FIG. 5–2. Crossability and sterility barriers between twenty-three sibling species in the *Gilia inconspicua* species complex. See Table 5–1 for geographical location, chromosome number, and taxonomic arrangement of the species. (From Grant, 1964, by permission. Copyrighted Academic Press, 1964.)

1962), *Erophila* (Winge, 1940), and *Elymus glauca* (Snyder, 1950, 1951). Reproductively isolated species that are morphologically indistinguishable or nearly so are called sibling species.

What do all these examples have to show us? The most important lesson is that there is no absolute correlation between morphological difference and reproductive isolation. Although in most cases populations that are distinctly different morphologically are also reproductively isolated, this is not true in all cases. These examples also show that the classical definition of the species and the biological definition are not strictly equivalent. The reason for this will become apparent if the process by which species are formed is analyzed.

Speciation: Some Theoretical Considerations

Speciation is the process by which new species are formed from other, ancestral ones. There are two major modes by which new species can originate. The first is by transformation in time of one species into another. This mode is called *phyletic speciation*. The second is the process by which one ancestral species gives rise to one or more species without necessarily losing its identity. This process is referred to as *multiplication of species* or *true speciation*. We will be concerned in this discussion with the latter process.

What is the general hypothesis regarding speciation? The most widely accepted hypothesis explaining the process of multiplication of species or true speciation is what has been called the *geographical theory of speciation* or sometimes also the *allopatric theory of speciation*, first enunciated by Moritz Wagner in 1868. Succinctly, it states that the first step in speciation is reproductive isolation brought about by physical (geographical) separation. A second step is the independent evolution of these reproductively isolated populations. If and when the ranges of the populations eventually merge again, the reproductive isolation persists because some other isolation mechanism such as genetic incompatibility has evolved, the speciation process is considered completed.

Four steps can be identified in the speciation process (Fig. 5–3): (1) separation of the original gene pool into two; (2) independent evolution of the two gene pools; (3) secondary merger; and (4) competition between the new gene pools. Let us analyze these separately.

Isolation

A group of interbreeding populations called a *gene pool* may become separated into two or more isolated gene pools as a result of changes in the environment. Apparently this separation results commonly from a shrinkage of the range of the species so that populations become physically completely reproductively isolated. This separation may also be the result of long-range dispersal when new populations become established beyond the range of pollination of the original gene pool. Both of these phenomena are common, and almost every species with an extended range has populations that are effectively reproductively isolated from the rest of the populations of the species.

The process of geographical isolation affects all kinds of plants. However, as we have already discussed in the preceding chapter, species that are self-

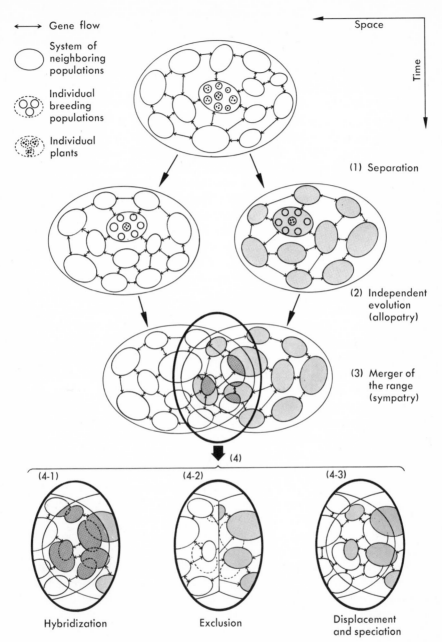

FIG. 5–3. The stages of the speciation process. (1) The original population gives rise to two isolated population systems that (2) evolve independently under different selection pressures. When (and if) they (3) merge their ranges partially or entirely, they may (4-1) hybridize, restoring the original situation of one species; or (4-2) they may exclude each other, restoring the case of two geographically isolated population systems; or (4-3) they may displace and form the new situation of two sympatric species. This last case can also occur if the species have differentiated before they merged their range.

pollinating have a greater chance of successful establishment after long-range dispersal. So do plants that are adapted to disturbed or open habitats.

Differentiation

By *differentiation* is meant the process by which two populations in isolation evolve in different directions so that they become morphologically and physiologically different. Differentiation does not necessarily follow upon isolation, although apparently it often does. The factors controlling the process of differentiation still need to be investigated in more detail. However, there seems to be ample evidence for the idea that populations will adapt closely to the conditions of the environment in which they are found. In chapter 3 some of the facts of ecogeographical differentiation were discussed, including results of experiments by various workers on ecotype formation. Ecotype formation is probably the first step in differentiation. In this connection, an interesting series of studies not yet discussed is that of Bradshaw and collaborators on lead-tolerant plants.

Agrostis tenuis is a common, self-incompatible, perennial grass that grows in a wide variety of habitats in temperate regions. In Britain populations of *Agrostis tenuis* are also found growing on mine workings in the vicinity of abandoned mines. These mine workings are high in lead concentration and toxic to most vegetation. Consequently, few plants are able to grow on them, including plants of *Agrostis tenuis* from normal soil. However, populations have evolved that are lead tolerant (Bradshaw, 1960). Tolerance does not appear to be induced by conditioning processes, is not lost in cultivation in the absence of the metal, and is heritable (Bradshaw, 1959; Bradshaw, McNeilly, and Gregory, 1965). In a study of the populations of the Goginon Mine in Wales, Bradshaw could demonstrate that the transition zone between lead-tolerant and intolerant populations is less than twenty meters wide. It was also demonstrated that the plants on each side of the zone have the same levels of tolerance and intolerance as the plants considerably further away from the boundary. Analysis of the ecological and historical factors indicate that the lead-tolerant forms must have developed recently and that they evolved in place, that is, within a few feet from the nontolerant forms and within pollination range. However, the selection pressures are apparently so strong that the hybrids have nowhere to become established. They are not able to tolerate the high lead content on one side of the line or the competition from the other plants on the other. Lack of hybrid survival constitutes in this case an absolute or almost absolute barrier to gene exchange. Similar situations with varying degrees of intermediacy have been reported for species adapted to serpentine and other soils: *Streptanthus* and other species (Kruckeberg, 1951, 1954, 1957, 1958), *Erigeron* (Mooney, 1967), and *Arctostaphylos* (Gottlieb, 1968). In all these instances there are two populations: a serpentine-tolerant and an intolerant one; no absolute isolating barrier exists between them, but hybrid establishment is not possible or it is restricted to a narrow zone.

These examples, in addition to pointing out the close adaptation of plants to the environment, also introduce a new factor, the role of disruptive selection (see Chapter 2). In the case of *Streptanthus* and *Arctostaphylos* the serpentine and nonserpentine plants differ morphologically, and it cannot be ascertained whether the present contact has always existed or is of recent origin due to expansion of the range of either or both species. However, in the case of *Agrostis* and probably also *Erigeron* the evidence points to differentiation having taken place without geographical separation. This is important information, because a point that has been and is still being discussed vigorously is whether geographical isolation is always necessarily a first condition for speciation. The data from *Agrostis* and other similar species appear to indicate that it is not.

Merger of the Range

The forces that lead to an overlapping of the ranges of two hitherto isolated populations are similar to those that lead to their separation. Basically these forces are environmental changes that lead to expansion of the range or migration of the population or population systems into an area previously not occupied. It is also possible that the evolution of the populations produces physiological or morphological changes (such as the development of a better seed dispersal apparatus) that are directly or indirectly responsible for expansion. This step is not a necessary condition in the process of speciation. However, when it takes place it leads to important interactions between the two hitherto separated units.

Range Overlap and Resulting Competition

The superposition of the range of the populations so that their members are within pollination range and the resulting interaction is the last step in the speciation process. However, the two populations that come together may have differentiated physiologically and genetically so that they will have different ecological requirements and so that their gametes will no longer fuse to form viable zygotes. In such cases the speciation process has been completed without interaction.

However, if the populations that come into contact have the same ecological requirements and also are capable of hybridizing, they will compete with each other. The result of this competition can have one of three outcomes:

1. One species outcompetes the other and the previous nonoverlap of the range is restored.

2. As a result of selection the two species divide the environment in such a way that they no longer compete and, at the same time, some kind of breeding barrier is established so that few or no hybrids are formed.

3. The two populations hybridize and form one interfertile population.

Exclusion Principle

When two hitherto separated populations come into renewed contact with each other, they may interact in two ways: (1) by competing for the resources of the environment and (2) by exchanging genes and forming hybrids and, if the hybrid is fertile, backcrosses.

Every breeding population has a specific set of environmental requirements such as habitat, soil, water tolerance, and so on. Whenever two populations share the requirement for some or all of the environmental components in a way that causes mutual interference, the two populations are competing for these resources. When two populations are competing they tend to displace each other; that is, the exact requirements of one or both populations will change in such a way that the competition is lessened. This is the essence of the so-called *exclusion principle* enunciated by the Russian biologist G. F. Gause in 1934: "No two forms can share exactly the same environmental requirements for an indefinite period of time, eventually one form will replace the other."

The species that form the native vegetation are all in a state of dynamic equilibrium, that is, they have divided the environment in such a way that interference is minimal. There always will be, of course, some competition for environmental factors because their supply is limited. For example, to take an extreme case, all plants require space to grow, and obviously where one plant is growing no other can. Light is also a requirement of all plants. In a forest the components of the various layers of vegetation, such as the canopy trees, the shrubs, and the herbs, have adjusted their photosynthetic light requirements so that they can coexist. Most trees cannot live in the shade whereas shrubs and herbs can, and herbs are able to exist with less light than shrubs. Also, all plants need water. However, some can exist where water is scarce and others cannot, and often adjustments are made for relatively small differences. For example, within the northern oak-beech forest swamp maples are always found where the soil moisture is highest.

However, competition can be best appreciated where there is lack of equilibrium. For example, any cultivated field or garden if not attended will very soon change its floristic composition. The cultivated plants are usually unable to reproduce and are replaced by annual plants adapted to the disturbed conditions that cultivation has created. However, after a few years, as the soil becomes more stabilized, the annual vegetation is gradually replaced by the vegetation typical of the region. Plants brought from other continents by man are, in general, agricultural weeds that cannot compete with the native vegetation under undisturbed conditions and are restricted in their distribution to fields and gardens, roadsides and railroad yards, and other such habitats created by man. The native vegetation adapted to another set of conditions cannot grow in these disturbed habitats.

Exclusion, that is, the elimination of one of the two hitherto separated populations, is one outcome of range overlap. The excluding population may be the ancestral one or it may be the descendant one. Another outcome of range overlap is displacement.

Displacement

When two semidifferentiated populations that share a particular environmental requirement come into contact they will compete, as has been pointed out above. Under such conditions the plants in each population that are most dissimilar in their requirements can grow where a minimum number of plants of the other population can grow. These plants will have a slight reproductive advantage over those in direct competition in that they will be largely or entirely free of competition, and by definition they will be favored by natural selection. In such a situation the two populations should slowly become more unlike in their requirements for the factor in question. This is the basic reasoning behind the hypothesis of character displacement (Wilson, 1965).

Two semidifferentiated populations coming into contact may hybridize, and the hybrids, if not totally sterile, will in turn backcross with the parental populations. Let us imagine the following example. Two populations have partially differentiated in relation to their tolerance to a certain harmful environmental factor. This tolerance is given by three pairs of genes, A, B, and C. A triple dominant plant, $AA\ BB\ CC$, has a range of tolerance between 90 and 100, one with five dominant genes between 80 and 90, and so on until a plant with all recessive genes has only a tolerance between 30 and 40. Populations 1 and 2 have differentiated toward the extremes of tolerance so that at the time of their reunion population 1 has the following gene frequencies: $A = 0.0$; $a = 1.0$; $B = 0.3$; $b = 0.7$; $C = 0.3$; and $c = 0.7$; whereas population 2 has the following gene frequencies: $A = 1.0$; $a = 0.0$; $B = 0.7$; $b = 0.3\ C = 0.7$; and $c = 0.3$. If the area where they become reunited has a gradient for this factor from 0 to 120 and the two populations tend to distribute themselves in accordance with their genotypic frequencies, the resultant distribution of plants of the two populations will approximate Fig. 5–4A (see also Table 5–2). If we assume that only plants that are in physical contact hybridize, that is, those in each population with tolerances between 50 and 80, some 35% of the plants of both populations will hybridize. They will give rise to a hybrid swarm with a genic frequency of 0.5 for all six alleles and the genotypic distribution shown in Figure 5–4B and Table 5–2. The hybrid seed can be either sterile or have any degree of fertility up to 100%. When the hybrid

TABLE 5–2

Genotypic Composition in Per Cent of the Total of Two Populations After One Generation of Reproduction Assuming No Fitness Difference Between Genotypes [see Text for Further Explanation]. In One Case All the Hybrid Seed Germinates and Forms Fertile Plants; in the Other Case No Hybrid Seed Germinates.

Genotype	Initial Composition		No Postfertilization Barrier			No Hybrid Seed Formed	
	Pop. 1	Pop. 2	Pop. 1	Pop. 2	Hybrids	Pop. 1	Pop. 2
aabbcc	0.2401	—	0.16807	—	0.0046	0.6561	—
aabbCc aaBbcc Aabbcc	0.4116	—	0.2881	—	0.0279	0.2916	—
aabbCC aaBbCc AabbCc aaBBcc AaBbcc AAbbcc	0.2646	0.0081	0.18522	0.0056	0.0563	0.1944	0.0001
aaBbCC AabbCC aaBBCc AAbbCc AaBBcc AABbcc	0.0756	0.0756	0.0529	0.0529	0.1125	0.0360	0.0360
aaBBCC AaBbCC AaBBCc AABbCc AAbbCC AABBcc	0.0081	0.2646	0.0056	0.18522	0.0563	0.0001	0.1944
aABBCC AABbCC AABBCc	—	0.4116	—	0.2881	0.0279	—	0.2916
AABBCC	—	0.2401	—	0.16807	0.0046	—	0.6561

seeds are absolutely sterile and consequently do not germinate, the effective populations, that is, the ones that are going to reproduce the two populations, are formed largely by the plants outside the area of overlap. In these plants the gene frequencies are as follows: population 1 (tolerance range 30–50): $A = 0.0$; $a = 1.0$; $B = 0.1$; $b = 0.9$; $C = 0.1$; $c = 0.9$. Population 2 (tolerance range 80–100): $A = 1.0$; $a = 0.0$; $B = 0.9$; $b = 0.1$; $C = 0.9$; $c = 0.1$. The change in the gene frequencies has been quite drastic in the direction of a fixation of the recessive genes in population 1 and the dominant in population

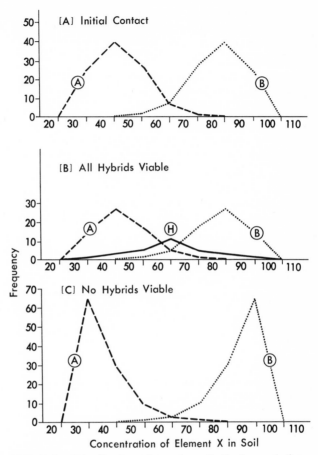

FIG. 5–4. Distribution of two hypothetical populations A and B with relation to an element X in the soil. Both populations are interfertile; they have, however, differentiated in isolation with relation to their tolerance to the element X (for genic frequencies, see text and Table 5–2). The assumptions are that the frequency of hybridizations is proportional to the degree of overlap of the populations, that breeding is random in the zone of overlap and that all pollinizations produce seed. (A) Initial frequency of the two populations in relation to the concentration of element X. (B) Frequency of the two populations after one generation assuming all hybrid seed to be fertile. No displacement has occurred; the proportion of parental types in relation to the previous generation has decreased however. (C) Frequency of the two populations after one generation assuming all hybrid seed to be inviable. Maximum displacement away from the zone of overlap has taken place.

2. If, however, the hybrid seed is completely fertile, the effect will be just the opposite. Through backcrosses allele *A*, which is absent in population 1, will be introduced into that population, and similarly allele *a* will be introduced into population 2. In the same way the frequencies of the two other pairs of alleles will tend toward more similar values in both populations. From this extreme hypothetical example it can be seen that character displacement is strongly influenced by the kind and effectiveness of the reproductive barrier between the two species.

Displacement in this example is ostensibly tied to an ecological factor. However, there has also been displacement in respect to reproductive components, because physical separation will reduce hybridization. In turn, reduced hybridization will reinforce displacement. In many cases displacement is largely toward a purely reproductive component. In effect, whenever the environment is mosaic, that is, when instead of a gradient there is a patternless mixture of various factors, a semidifferentiated population that comes into contact with another population and forms sterile hybrids will be at a reproductive disadvantage, because part of its offspring is sterile. In such a situation fitness can be increased in two ways: (1) by an increase in the fertility of the hybrid and (2) by a reduction of hybridization. Which of these two strategies is selected depends basically on two factors: the amount of hybridization and the fertility of the hybrid, each of which, in turn, but particularly the first, is influenced by other factors, such as pollination systems, population size, degree of seed dispersal, life cycle, environmental fluctuations, and environmental heterogeneity.

Character displacement takes place only in the area of contact. Consequently, away from the area of species overlap the two species involved should look more alike than they do in the area of overlap. A good example is furnished by two species of rock nuthatches, *Sitta neumayer* and *Sitta tephronata*. The former species ranges from the Balkans in Europe eastward through the western half of Iran, and the latter ranges from Turkestan west to Armenia. The two species overlap in several sectors of Iran. They are morphologically very similar in their separate zones, but they diverge in the zones of overlap, where *S. neumayer* shows a distinct reduction in overall size, beak length, and intensity of a prominent facial stripe, characters that are unchanged in *S. tephronata*. These characters serve for species recognition, and their displacement in the zones of overlap most likely has the effect of discouraging hybridization.

In summary, from the evolutionary point of view speciation can be viewed as a process by which certain groups of breeding populations adapt closely to certain environmental situations. A species is therefore basically a group of populations with characteristics that allow it to persist in time by successfully utilizing the resources of the environment and producing sufficient offspring generation after generation.

From the point of view of the taxonomist, the problem is how to differentiate between species. In those cases where the speciation process has been completed and the resultant species are ecologically, physiologically, and morphologically different and also reproductively isolated, there is no problem. However, in those instances where the speciation process has been set in motion and there are two partially differentiated, partially isolated sets of populations, no absolute criterion indicates whether the process of speciation has proceeded far enough for the two population systems to be indeed two different evolutionary units. Genetic isolation can be tested experimentally by cross-pollinating the populations whose specific status is being tested. One can also test ecological and physiological differentiation experimentally by growing population samples under different environments and measuring their relative performance. Finally, morphological differentiation can be assessed by observation and measurement. However, these tests are time-consuming and expensive, and in the great majority of cases the question of total differentiation is too trivial to warrant the effort necessary to answer it quantitatively.

The usual procedure is to assess carefully the degree of morphological difference and to correlate it with as many ancillary data as are easily available. If the population samples under study show enough morphological difference for most or all individuals to be identified as members of one or the other population and, furthermore, if it can be shown that the morphological difference is not biologically trivial, then the two populations are considered to be different species. Otherwise, they are classed as members of the same species.

Chapter 6

Hybridization

Strictly speaking, hybridization is synonymous with outcrossing. Thus, whenever a zygote is formed by the union of an egg with a sperm from another plant, a hybrid is formed. The sperm may come from a plant in the same population, from a plant in another population of the same species, or from a different species. To distinguish between these different cases we will here restrict the use of the term *hybridization* to crosses between plants presumed to belong to different species. For crosses within the same species the term *recombination* will be used.

Hybridization is relatively common in the plant kingdom. Many species of plants, sometimes even those belonging to different genera and subfamilies, can be hybridized artificially (Adams and Anderson, 1958). The numerous species of plants that can be hybridized indicate that barriers to fertilization (essentially the inability of pollen to grow and germinate on foreign styles) are slow to develop in angiosperms and that they usually develop after physiological and morphological divergence has taken place. However, the fact that most hybrids between distinct taxa show some kind of loss of fertility indicates that a certain amount of genetic isolation accompanies morphological and physiological divergence.

Role of Hybridization in Evolution

Hybridization can occur whenever two species that possess no genetic sterility barrier are within pollination range of each other. Pollination range is defined as the distance within which most of the pollen of a species is dispersed. The hybrids that are formed usually combine the characteristics of both species, morphologically, physiologically, and ecologically. This means that if the parents have different requirements and tolerances such as for water, soil, light, or any other characteristic of the environment, the hybrid will probably not be able to grow successfully in the environment of either parent. However, in the area where the habitats occupied by the two parental populations come into contact, the physical habitat is often intermediate. Here the hybrids may successfully become established. Also, and perhaps more commonly, the hybrids become established in areas of disturbance, such as clearings, erosion gullies, cliffs, and so on. In areas of disturbance the conditions required by the parental species are not met in their entirety, but the somewhat modified and intermediate requirements of the hybrids often make them successful inhabitants of such areas. Man in recent times has been a major source of disturbed habitats, but phenomena such as glaciations, mountain building, and erosion have created disturbed habitats in the geological past.

Introgressive Hybridization

However, the evolutionary role of hybridization depends on the effect that hybridization has on the genetic composition of the parental populations and not necessarily on the frequency with which they are formed. That is, in most cases of hybridization it is not the hybrids but the backcrosses of the hybrids with the parents that play an evolutionary role. This process of backcrossing is known as *introgressive hybridization* (Anderson, 1949). By introgressive hybridization, genes from one species can be introduced into populations of another species. Anderson (1949, 1953) has repeatedly suggested that in cases of introgressive hybridization the backcrosses are favored by natural selection because of the new genes they carry.

The individual plants of a breeding population are more or less closely adapted to the environment in which they grow. In each generation mutation and recombination will produce individuals with genotypes closely resembling the parents and also individuals differing from them more or less. In a stable environment most of the seedlings that survive to maturity will have a genotype and phenotype similar to the parental generation; in a changing environment the offspring will not resemble their parents quite as much. The degree to which the offspring generation will differ from the parental generation depends on the degree of recombination (and all the factors that control recombination) and the intensity of selection, as has already been explained (Chapters 2 and 3). The greater the genetic recombination, the higher the probability that the offspring will not resemble their parents; the stronger the intensity of selection, the more genetic change will occur. If selection is stabilizing, the changes will be minimal and will be largely genotypic; if selection is directional, the changes will probably be of greater magnitude and will be reflected both in the genotype and in the phenotype (page 24).

Hybridization introduces new genes into a population and consequently increases the probability of genetic change. It acts as a factor that increases variability.

Effect of Hybridization and Introgression: The Sunflower Example

An excellent example of the role of hybridization in evolution is that of the sunflowers studied by Heiser (Anderson, 1952; Heiser, 1961). This genus of American plants comprises four more or less distinct groups (Heiser *et al.*, 1962): (1) eleven or twelve species of taprooted desert perennials. They are all diploid with seventeen pairs of chromosomes and are found only in North America; (2) forty or more North American species of perennial plants that grow from crown buds, rhizomes, or tubers, and are either diploid, tetraploid, or hexaploid; (3) seventeen shrubby species from South America, two of them diploid, the others unknown cytologically; (4) seventeen species of North American annuals. There is now positive evidence that of the fifty North American species of *Helianthus*, twenty-five are involved in hybridization with one or frequently several other species (Heiser, 1961). The crosses seem to be confined largely to species within each of the groups.

The annual species are especially interesting, particularly the common sunflower, *Helianthus annuus*. This species is found in central and western North America from southern Canada to northern Mexico. Morphologically the common sunflower is quite variable, not only within but especially between populations. Heiser (1954) subdivided the species into three subspecies and one variety: subspecies *lenticularis*, subspecies *texanus*, subspecies *annuus*, which includes the cultivated sunflower, variety *macrocarpus*. Subspecies *annuus* is the ruderal or weedy sunflower common in the middle western United States, particularly in railroad yards and vacant lots in cities and towns; subspecies *lenticularis*, on the other hand, is the wild sunflower of roadsides and abandoned fields in the west and southwest of the United States. Finally, subspecies *texanus* is restricted to eastern Texas. The story of the probable origin of these three forms is a fine example of the role of hybridization in evolution.

The ancestral form of the sunflower is not known with certainty. However, on the basis of extensive studies, Heiser (1954) postulates that subspecies *lenticularis* of western North America is more like the original form of the species than any other living subspecies. This subspecies, according to Heiser, gave rise to subspecies *annuus* under the indirect influence of man. The seeds of subspecies *lenticularis* were gathered for food by various tribes of Indians (Heiser, 1951b), and the sunflower may have become an early Indian camp weed adapted to disturbed areas around the camps and villages. In time, either through conscious or unconscious selection by man, subspecies *lenticularis* could have given rise to the slightly larger forms that developed into subspecies *annuus*. Subspecies *annuus* variety *macrocarpa*, the cultivated sunflower, differs basically from variety *annuus* by a single mutation that restricts branching and leads to the production of a single or a very few large heads. Man has, of course, in addition selected forms for higher yield, especially in recent times.

The history of the third subspecies, *H. annuus* subspecies *texanus*, is more involved. It appears to have arisen after the introduction by either man or natural causes of either subspecies *lenticularis* or *annuus* into Texas. Today *H. annuus* subspecies *texanus* is very common on roadsides and abandoned fields, especially in central Texas. In eastern Texas grows another annual species of sunflower, *Helianthus debilis* variety *cucumerifolius*, found both as a roadside weed and in undisturbed sites. Where *Helianthus debilis* variety *cucumerifolius* and *H. annuus* subspecies *texanus* grow together, occasionally a few hybrid plants are found. These are more stunted in growth than the parental species that grow in the vicinity and are highly sterile, although they produce a very small proportion of viable pollen. The variation of *Helianthus annuus* in eastern Texas (Table 6–1) is clearly in the direction of *H. debilis* (Heiser, 1951a) in regard to the large proportion of leaves with jagged serration, speckled stems, small head diameters, small achenes, low number of ray flowers, small bract width, and the tendency to branch from the base. Consequently, it has been postulated (Heiser, 1951a) that variety *texanus* arose as a result of hybridization and introgression of *H. debilis* variety *cucumerifolius* with *H. annuus* subspecies *lenticularis* or subspecies *annuus* when this last species was introduced into Texas. In addition to the morphological characters that *H. annuus* acquired from *H. debilis*, it presumably also acquired physiological characteristics that adapted it to withstand better the climate and environment of Texas, characteristics acquired by *H. debilis* over many years of existence in Texas.

TABLE 6–1

Comparison of the Number of Ray Flowers and Disk Diameter of the Common Sunflower *Helianthus annuus*, and the Texas Sunflower, *H. debilis* var. *cucumerifolius*. [Data from Heiser, 1951a.]

Species	Locality	No. Ray Flowers	Disk Diameter (cm.)
H. debilis, var.	Nacogdoches Co., Texas	13.7	1.62
cucumerifolius	Frio Co., Texas	15.7	1.84
	Houston Co., Texas	19.0	2.24
H. annuus	Galveston Co., Texas	17.3	2.30
	Frio Co., Texas	20.4	2.58
	Galveston Co., Texas	22.0	3.28
	Collin Co., Texas*	23.2	3.60
	Pittsburgh Co., Okla.*	25.9	3.54

Note how populations of *H. debilis* acquire more rays and a larger disk as they move north and west (*H. annuus* territory), whereas *H. annuus* populations lose rays and acquire a smaller disk as they move south and east (*H. debilis* territory).

* These populations are outside the territory of *H. debilis*.

At the other end of the distribution of *Helianthus annuus* in California, a similar phenomenon of hybridization can be observed. The sunflower is a relatively recent resident of California. It was probably introduced first by the Indians, who used the seeds as food and who also used the flower in their religious rites. It is likely that in the beginning it was restricted in its distribution to disturbed sites around Indian camps. In the last hundred years or so, as a result of the activities of European man, disturbed sites have multiplied enormously in California, and so has the sunflower, which is now very widespread along roadsides and railroad tracks and as a weed in cultivated fields. *Helianthus bolanderi* is a sunflower native to California and Oregon. It grows in two kinds of habitats. One race is found in the serpentine outcrops of the coastal ranges. These serpentine outcrops are soils with an extremely low calcium level and a high content of magnesium and heavy metals. They sustain a highly specialized flora (Kruckeberg, 1954). In addition, *H. bolanderi* occurs as a ruderal weed in the central and northern valleys of California at the same sites as *annuus*. In a detailed study Heiser (1949) has shown that these two species hybridize occasionally. Although the hybrid is largely sterile, it can produce some good pollen. According to Heiser, when *H. annuus* was introduced into California it hybridized with *H. bolanderi*, which probably was then restricted to the serpentine outcrops. From repeated crosses and backcrosses of these two species emerged a form of *H. annuus* that resembled *H. bolanderi* (Table 6–2, Fig. 6–1) and adapted well to the California environment, presumably by borrowing genes from *H. bolanderi*. From

TABLE 6–2

Comparison of the Number of Ray Flowers and Disk Diameter of the Common Sunflower *Helianthus annuus*, and the California Sunflower, *H. bolanderi*. [Data from Heiser 1949.]

Species	Mean No. Ray Flowers	Disk Diameter [cm.]
H. bolanderi—serpentine	12.7*	1.70*
H. bolanderi—valley	14.8*	2.07*
H. bolanderi × *H. annuus* hybrid	14–20**	2–3**
H. annuus, Calif.	18.2*	2.41*
H. annuus, non-Calif.	20.7*	2.98*

* Mean value for garden grown plants (29 to 61 plants measured according to population).
** Range of values for 6 plants.

introgression of genes of *H. annuus* into *H. bolanderi* emerged the form of *H. bolanderi* that is capable of growing in disturbed habitats.

In addition to *H. bolanderi* and *H. debilis* variety *cucumerifolius*, the range of *Helianthus annuus* overlaps with other annual species. One of them is *H. petiolaris*, a species that is widespread in the western United States and occasionally eastward with a distribution similar to *H. annuus*, although this last species is more widespread. Although both species grow together in many

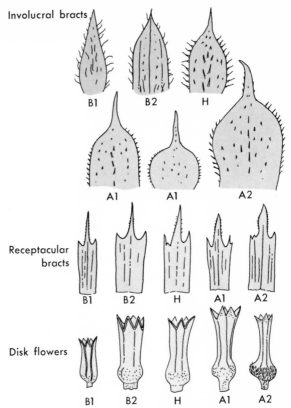

FIG. 6–1. Effect of hybridization on morphological characteristics of species, in this case *H. annuus* and *H. bolanderi*. B1, *Helianthus bolanderi*, serpentine race; B2, *H. bolanderi*, nonserpentine race, presumed to have introgressed with *H. annuus*; H, natural hybrid between *H. annuus* and *H. bolanderi*; A1, *H. annuus*, from California, presumed to have introgressed with *H. bolanderi*; A2, *H. annuus* from St. Louis, Mo., outside the range of *H. bolanderi*, and consequently free of any contamination by *H. bolanderi*. Note how the presumed introgressed types look more like the hybrid than either of the "pure" species. (From Heiser 1949, by permission.)

places, there seem to be some slightly different ecological preferences (Heiser, 1947). In general, *H. annuus* seems to be more restricted to heavy soils and *H. petiolaris* to sandy soils. In addition, while *H. petiolaris* comes into bloom in June and blooms through July and into August, *H. annuus* generally does not bloom until July and continues to bloom into September, restricting somewhat the opportunities for gene exchange. Hybrid swarms between these

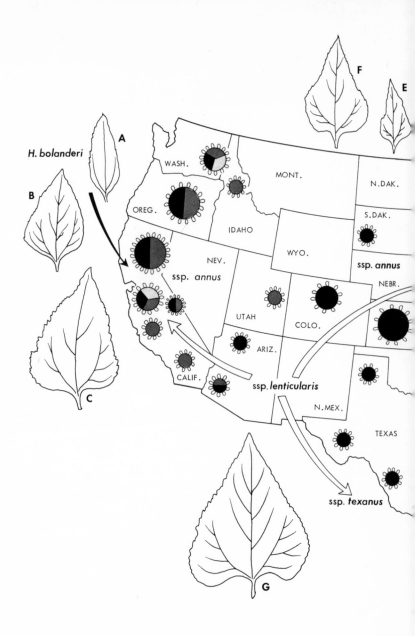

FIG. 6–2. Probable evolution of *Helianthus annuus* in the United States according to Heiser. Subspecies *lenticularis* (or the derived subspecies *annuus*) spread from the southwestern United States to California where it hybridized with *H. bolanderi*. Subspecies *lenticularis* (or subsp. *annuus*) spread also to the midwest where it hybridized with *H. petiolaris*, and to Texas where it hybridized with *H. debilis var. cucumerifolius* giving rise to subspecies *texanus*. Differentiation as a result of selection was also taking place as can be seen by the different size heads, anther color, and number of ray flowers. Diagrams of heads drawn proportional

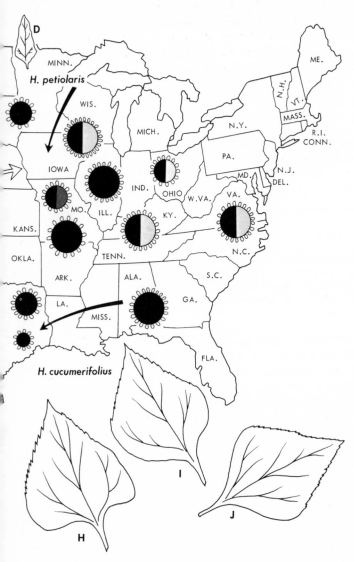

to values of natural populations; "petals," each representing two ray flowers; shading represents anther color: black, purple anthers; hatching, red anthers; white, black anthers; combinations, mixtures of colors in the population. A–J: outline of leaves: A. *H. bolanderi*; B. *H. annuus* × *H. bolanderi*; C. *H. annuus ssp. annuus*; D. *H. petiolaris*; E. *H. petiolaris* × *H. annuus*; F. *H. annuus ssp. annuus*; G. *H. annuus ssp. lenticularis*; H. *H. annuus ssp. texanus*; I. *H. annuus* × *H. debilis var. cucumerifolius*; J. *H. debilis var. cucumerifolius*. (Data from Heiser 1947, 1949, 1951a, 1954.)

two species are not frequent, but have been observed several times. Again, the hybrid is quite sterile, but produces some viable pollen, and consequently introgression has occurred. Introgressed populations of *H. petiolaris* have broader and more serrated leaves, hispid involucral bracts, and a general increase in the size of all the parts of the plant. Populations of *H. annuus* subjected to introgression from *H. petiolaris*, on the other hand, have narrower leaves, narrower involucral bracts, smaller heads, a more densely pubescent chaff, and a reduced number of ray flowers (Table 6–3, Fig. 6–2).

TABLE 6–3

Comparison of the Number of Ray Flowers and Disk Diameter of the Common Sunflower, *Helianthus annuus*, and *H. petiolaris*. [Data from Heiser, 1947.]

Species	No. Ray Flowers*	Disk Diameter** (cm.)
H. petiolaris	13–16	2.3
H. petiolaris × *H. annuus*	15–21	2.9
H. annuus	21–30	3.3

* Range for several plants grown in the garden.
** Mean for populations from East St. Louis.

From these three examples of hybridization and introgression a pattern emerges that has been observed in several other species. The four species of sunflowers that have been discussed are most likely to have developed in isolation from each other. Under these circumstances they differentiated and became adapted to specific ecological conditions. Nevertheless, they did not acquire total genetic isolation. When *H. annuus* increased its range (probably as a result of man's activities), it came into contact with the three other species. Hybrids were formed and they in turn backcrossed with the parents, transmitting genes from one species to the other. Some of the genes so transmitted conferred on the recipient species characteristics that made it better adapted to the new environment. Because *H. annuus* was the invading species, it probably acquired physiological characteristics that allowed it to adapt better to the conditions of Texas, California, and the Midwest. It in turn probably conferred on the other three species characteristics that permitted these species to grow on disturbed soils (Fig. 6–2). Harlan and De Wet (1963) have termed species such as *H. annuus, compilospecies*, "robber species," because through hybridization they "borrow" genes from native species and in this way become more widely adapted.

It can be seen, then, that the probable role of introgressive hybridization in plant evolution is to enable some species to acquire genes from other species and in this way increase their fitness and adaptation to new habitats.

Hybridization, Life Cycle, and the Selection of Breeding Barriers

How can two species that hybridize when they come into contact maintain their identity in the presence of gene flow, which tends to mix their genic patrimony? The inability of the hybrid to grow in the habitat of either parent and its restriction to a belt of intermediate or disturbed conditions is one answer. The selection of mechanisms that will restrict hybridization still further is another possible way of protecting the identity of the parental species.

Helianthus annuus represents one outcome of hybridization: the formation of a belt or zone of introgressed genotypes such as *H. annuus* variety *texanus*. Two species of sage of the genus *Salvia* in California represent another common situation, that of two species living side by side, capable of interbreeding and forming vigorous hybrids. However, the hybrids are very few in actuality, and there is apparently very little introgression.

Salvia apiana and *S. mellifera* are two species that grow in the coastal sage communities of southern and central California (Fig. 6–3). Their ranges

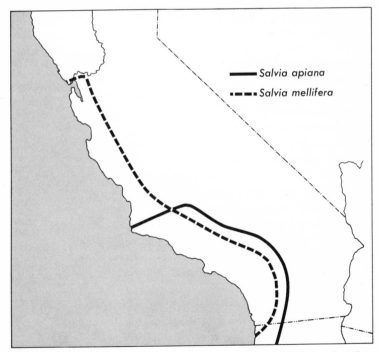

FIG. 6–3. Map of California showing the distribution of *Salvia mellifera* and *Salvia apiana* and the area of overlap of the two species. (From Epling, 1947.)

overlap in the area between Santa Barbara and the Mexican border. *Salvia apiana* shows a slight preference for the drier soils, although the two species often grow intermixed (Epling, 1947a; Anderson and Anderson, 1954). *Salvia mellifera* blooms earlier, approximately from April to the end of May, whereas *S. apiana* blooms from the middle of May to the end of June (Grant and Grant, 1964). Consequently there is little overlap in their blooming times. *Salvia mellifera* has a smaller flower whereas *S. apiana* has a much larger flower (Fig. 6–4). Finally, whereas the first species is typically pollinated by a variety of small bees, flies, and butterflies, *S. apiana* is pollinated mainly by larger carpenter bees. These ecological and mechanical differences combine to keep the two species reproductively isolated. Nevertheless, hybrids are formed occasionally, most frequently in disturbed habitats. When these hybrids grow to maturity they are only partially fertile. Although in such instances some introgression occurs, it does not seem to be very widespread (Epling, 1947a).

The two species of sage illustrate how species with no absolute genetic isolation barriers can grow side by side with little or no hybridization. This example also shows that there is no one absolute reproductive isolating barrier, but a large number of partial barriers that reinforce each other to produce almost total reproductive isolation. Although few cases have been studied in such detail as that of *Salvia*, many others are known. Many species of oaks are capable of interbreeding, so are many species of willows, poplars, and birches. However, although hybrids are formed, the parental species maintain their identity and do not form homogeneous hybrid swarms. As a matter of fact, it can be said that many species of closely related trees are interfertile, but nevertheless do not hybridize extensively.

However, natural interspecific hybridization is rare in annual plants. The probable reason for this has to do with still another facet of the phenomenon of hybridization: the effect that the fertility of the hybrid has on the total fitness of the population.

In order to survive, any population of plants has to replace those mature and reproducing individuals that die. It is well known that plants produce a great excess of seeds over the number that actually germinate and become mature plants. Consequently, under normal circumstances the production of a few or even a large number of more or less inviable seeds does not necessarily result in an immediate decrease in the number of the offspring. This is particularly true with long-lived trees, because very few individuals have to be replaced every year. However, annuals have to reproduce the population in its entirety every year. The production of a large number of hybrids could therefore be detrimental to an annual species, particularly if the backcrosses led to the formation of less fertile individuals. Because annual plant species usually live in areas with large climatic changes from year to year, where certain seasons may allow the growth of only a small number of individuals, the possible detrimental effects of hybridization is accentuated. This may

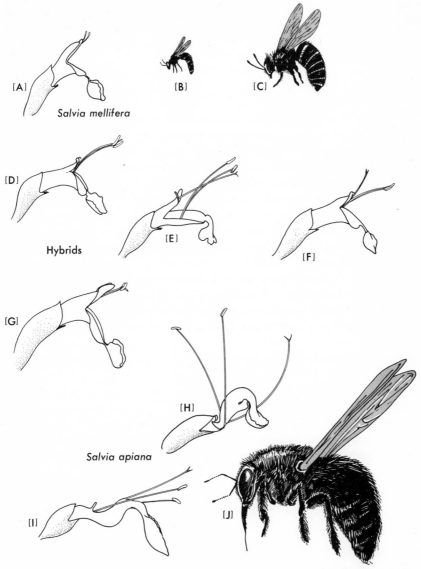

FIG. 6–4. Flowers of *Salvia mellifera*, *S. apiana*, and their hybrids and backcrosses, and some specific pollinators. A. *Salvia mellifera*; B. *Chloralictus* sp., a small-sized solitary bee that pollinates *S. mellifera*; C. *Anthophora* sp., a medium-sized bee, pollinator of *S. mellifera*; D. F₁ hybrid between *S. mellifera* × *S. apiana*; E–G. backcrosses of D. to both parents; H–I. *S. apiana*, untripped and tripped position of flower; J. *Xylocopa brasilianorum*, a pollinator of *S. apiana*. It can readily be seen that the different size of the flowers of these two species and their pollinators act as an isolating mechanism. (Redrawn from Epling, 1947a, and Grant and Grant, 1964, by permission.)

explain why among annuals the species are usually well demarcated genetically, even when they are not well demarcated morphologically. This is well
illustrated by genera such as *Gilia* and *Clarkia* (pages 77 and 104), in which
interspecific hybrids are often very sterile and, more important, where natural
hybridization seems to be rare or nonexistent.

Hybridization and Reproductive Isolation

Hybridization in plants is a very important phenomenon. Basically it enables
species to acquire new genetic material from outside sources when changes in
selective pressures arise either from the migration of the species into new
habitats or from long-term changes in the environment. However, too high
an incidence of hybridization could lead to the opposite effect, a complete
breakdown of the unique genetic patrimony of the species, making it less
rather than more adapted to a particular environment. This is an occasional
result of hybridization. More often the effect of hybridization is less drastic
because of mechanisms that prevent indiscriminate mixing. These mechanisms are (1) an inability of the hybrid and the backcrosses to compete
successfully with the original species in all but a few special habitats (such as
disturbed sites or areas with environment intermediate between that of the
two species) and (2) a reduced fertility of the hybrid and of the backcrosses
that slows down the mixing process. However, if the hybrid is successful in
competing with the flora and becomes established and utilizes the resources of
the environment, selection for higher fertility in the hybrid should occur.

In conclusion, hybridization can lead to the formation of new or modified
species, or it can lead indirectly to the formation of isolation barriers as we
saw in the previous chapter. Or, as is more often the case, it can proceed
largely in a passive manner with slight effects, such as the formation of
occasional hybrid swarms in areas of disturbed or intermediate habitats.

Chapter 7

The Species Problem and Classification

To group like with like is basic to the human need for assuring adequate communication. Our language is a series of symbols that represent groups of like things; our thought processes are based on the handling of symbols and situations that can be broken down into, or are themselves a representation of, a series of like situations. Grouping like with like is the essence of classification, and without this classification no communication of any sort would be possible, nor would a rational perception of the world.

The systematic and uniform application of this process of classification to the biological world was by necessity the first step in the development of scientific biology. In order to deal with the tremendous diversity of organisms, man had to codify this diversity somehow and apply some uniform rules to the naming of organisms. As we have seen, Linnaeus introduced a useful nomenclatural system (1753) that was widely used, and, since the end of the nineteenth century, uniform rules have been adopted and followed by almost all botanists.

However, species are not static objects, but complex systems of populations that are variable in time and space. Consequently, in most cases they cannot be defined in terms of a single characteristic as can an inanimate or manmade object. For example, a certain make of car can be clearly separated from another by one of several characteristics, such as shape, or performance, or size. Each characteristic is present in all the cars of that model so that one model can easily be separated from any other model. However, the existence of a group of interbreeding populations does not imply that all the populations and their members are necessarily alike in all characteristics. Furthermore, speciation is usually a gradual process and many populations of plants are in the process of differentiation and therefore cannot easily and unmistakably be classified as part of the parental species or as a new, derived species.

Abrupt Speciation

To complicate matters further, sometimes among plants speciation occurs abruptly rather than in the gradual way explained in Chapter 5. This usually occurs as a result of the doubling of the chromosome number of the plant, a process called *polyploidy*, or as a result of special evolutionary mechanisms, such as what is known as *catastrophic selection*.

Polyploidy

The subject of polyploidy will be covered more extensively in Chapter 9 (page 145). Polyploidy can be defined as the phenomenon that results in doubling of the number of chromosomes of a plant. The resultant plant in most cases is incapable of forming fertile offspring with members of the ancestral diploid population. It has therefore acquired instant reproductive isolation, and, if it is capable of reproducing and of finding an ecological situation that it can exploit, a new species has been formed. Among the angiosperms close to 40% of all species appear to be polyploid, so that polyploidy is a very important phenomenon indeed.

Polyploids are basically of two kinds (Fig. 7–1): (1) autopolyploids, which are the result of the doubling of the chromosomes of a normal plant, and (2) allopolyploids, which are the result of the doubling of the chromosomes of a hybrid plant. This latter kind is apparently more frequent. The probability of establishment of an allopolyploid is higher for cytological reasons (meiosis is more likely to be normal), and also because the hybrid may have novel characteristics that will allow it to exploit habitats not open to either of the parents.

From the taxonomic point of view polyploidy presents special problems. Autopolyploids are morphologically very similar to the parental population; allopolyploids are intermediate, or combine the characteristics of the two parental species. In the latter case blurring of differences between species occurs, and in the former case a noncorrelation between morphology and isolation exists.

Catastrophic Selection

Apparently in some instances very rapid speciation can take place leading to genetic isolation with little or no morphological differentiation but without polyploidy, a phenomenon known as *catastrophic selection* (H. Lewis, 1962). The best example is furnished by the genus *Clarkia* of the family Onagraceae.

Clarkia is a group of plants found in the western United States centered

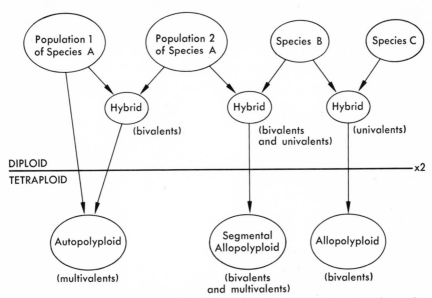

FIG. 7–1. The various types of polyploidy. Autopolyploidy results from the doubling of the chromosomes of a plant, or an *intraspecific* hybrid. Because autopolyploids have four sets of identical or nearly identical chromosomes, they are expected to form associations of four (quadrivalents) at meiosis, and as a result they are expected to be sterile. Allopolyploids result from the doubling of the chromosomes of an *interspecific* hybrid between two relatively unrelated species. The diploid hybrid is sterile because the chromosomes of the two species are nonhomologous and will not pair; however, when the chromosomes are doubled, bivalents can again be formed and the allopolyploid will be fertile. A segmental allopolyploid is halfway between an autopolyploid and an allopolyploid, in that the chromosomes of the two species are related enough to form bivalents in the diploid hybrid, but also form bivalents at the tetraploid level. (See also Fig. 9–6, page 149.)

around California. They have been the subject of intense biosystematic studies over the last twenty years by Harlan Lewis and his students. In the process, interspecific crosses have been attempted between most of the species. The cytological analysis of the hybrids so obtained showed that many species differ quite drastically in the linear order of the genes. This is illustrated particularly well by *Clarkia franciscana* (Lewis and Raven, 1958a, b). This species is known from only one locality, a serpentine-covered slope overlooking the Golden Gate at the east end of the Presidio in San Francisco, California (Fig. 7–2). The species is morphologically similar to two other species, *C. rubricunda* and *C. amoena*, that occur close by. The first of these species is found along the coast and in the valleys of the California coast ranges from northern San Luis Obispo County to just north of San Francisco Bay in Marin County. *Clarkia amoena* replaces *C. rubricunda* in central Marin County and continues northward along the coast to British Columbia

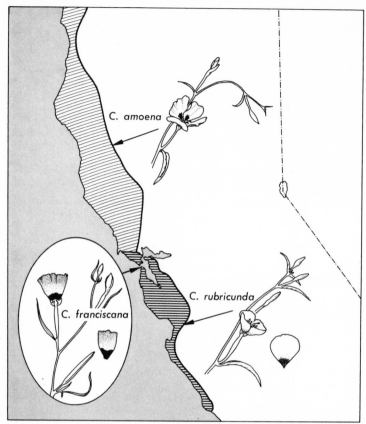

FIG. 7–2. Distribution of *Clarkia amoena*, *C. franciscana*, and *C. rubricunda* in California. Note how morphologically similar the three species are. The best distinguishing feature is the petal, particularly the spot, which is bright red and present near the center in *C. amoena*, is well defined, conspicuous, reddish purple and basal in *C. franciscana*, and is not so well defined and merges somewhat in *C. rubricunda*. (From H. Lewis, 1958, by permission.)

and Vancouver Island. Interspecific hybrids among *Clarkia franciscana*, *C. amoena*, and *C. rubricunda* were made by Lewis and Raven in all combinations to determine the fertility of the hybrids and to study the differences in chromosome architecture as indicated by chromosome pairing at meiosis. The fertility of the pollen in every case was not more than 2%. The pairing of the chromosomes in the hybrids showed that the chromosomes of these three species differed drastically in the arrangement of homologous segments. *Clarkia franciscana* differs from *C. rubricunda* by at least three large translocations and four paracentric inversions, and from *C. amoena* by at least two translocations and two or more paracentric inversions, as well as possibly by a series of smaller rearrangements. *Clarkia amoena*, in turn, differs from *C. rubricunda* by three translocations and two inversions. The chromosomal changes are of an entirely different magnitude than in the case of most species such as in *Glandularia*, mentioned in Chapter 5. (See also Fig. 9–5.)

When two closely related species or populations differ in the order of the genes in their chromosomes, it is obvious that in one or both of the differing species or populations changes have taken place in the architecture of the chromosomes, because the common ancestor of these species or populations must have had one arrangement only (at least at one time). How does this take place? The usual assumption is that a small chromosomal change takes place in a plant of a population that gives that plant a higher fitness. In time all plants of the population will have the new chromosomal arrangement. By the repetition of this process the populations can become quite distinct cytologically. These changes presumably are accompanied by morphological and physiological changes as the populations become adapted to different ecological conditions.

Does the great dissimilarity in the chromosomal arrangement of the genes between *Clarkia franciscana*, *C. amoena*, and *C. rubricunda* and their great morphological similarity suggest that they have originated in ways other than by the gradual accumulation of small changes? Whenever the arrangement of the order of the genes in a chromosome of a plant is changed, crossing-over within the altered segment in a plant that is heterozygous for this change (and the progeny of any cross of the plant with the new arrangement and one with unaltered chromosomes will be heterozygous for the change) will produce two sterile gametes out of the four gametes that are the normal product of meiosis. If the altered segment is small, the probability of a cross-over occurring within the segment is very small; consequently a cross-over will not occur in most cells undergoing meiosis, and the new arrangement can become established in the population. However, if the segment is large, the converse is true. Therefore, the probability that the chromosomal arrangements of *Clarkia franciscana* are the result of a small accumulation of small changes is indeed very low, because the repeated establishment of small chromosomal changes without corresponding changes in morphology is an improbable event. H. Lewis (1962; Lewis and Raven, 1958b) has therefore hypothesized a mechanism that he termed *catastrophic selection*.

According to this hypothesis, under certain unknown conditions (environmental stress [draught?] or "mutator genotypes" [genotypes that produce a high frequency of mutations] have been mentioned as possible causes) drastic chromosomal rearrangements take place in a plant. If a plant with such a drastic chromosomal rearrangement becomes detached from the population, it can establish a population with a new chromosomal arrangement that is genetically isolated from the ancestral population from its very inception.

What forces bring about such drastic changes in some cases and so little in others is still a mystery, particularly because some species that have been isolated for millions of years have not developed any genetic or chromosomal differences. One possible such case is that of the two species of sycamores, *Platanus orientalis* and *Platanus occidentalis*. The first of these species is a native of the Middle East, the second of eastern North America. They are morphologically very distinct and also physiologically so, because they grow in different climatic regions. How long these two species have been isolated is impossible to say with any certainty, but it is likely that it has been at least from the end of the Tertiary Period, a million or more years. The artificial hybrid between these species, known as *P. acerifolia* and widely cultivated as an ornamental tree, is vigorous and highly fertile and has a normal meiosis (Sax, 1933), indicating that no drastic changes in the order of the genes has taken place.

The only general conclusion that can be drawn is that when two populations are isolated, physiological, morphological, and genetic differentiation proceeds differently in each case. The forces that control differentiation are not known in specific terms. In general terms, these forces are (1) the degree of environmental change to which the species adjusts and (2) the genetic system of each species, which controls and determines the way a species responds to the environmental changes. Basically the problem is one of relative rates of evolution of two isolated populations or population systems.

The Biological Species Concept and the Evolutionary Unit

In the previous two chapters a review has been attempted of some of the salient features of the mechanisms of speciation and of the role of hybridization in the evolution of plants. It must be clear to the reader by now that plant species are not necessarily genetically isolated from other plant species. As a matter of fact, most closely related perennial species are not genetically isolated, and although genetic isolation is more common among annuals and perennial herbs, even among them it is by no means universal. Because this situation appears to be different from that found among animals, it requires further discussion.

"Leaky" Isolation Barriers

Table 7–1 tabulates the major kinds of isolation mechanisms found among plants. Of these, the only truly absolute isolating barriers are (1) gametic incompatibility, that is, the inability of the pollen to germinate on the style or of the sperm of one species to form a viable seedling with the egg of a second species, and (2) absolute hybrid sterility, the incapacity of the hybrid to form viable gametes. All other barriers are likely to break down and may be termed "leaky" isolating barriers. Species that are geographically separated may come together in the course of time; some pollen grains may in some

TABLE 7-1

Isolation Mechanisms.

Prefertilization	Reduction of contact	1. Geographical separation 2. Ecological separation
	Reduction of mating frequency	3. Pollen incompatibility* (gametic isolation) 4. Inbreeding and asexual reproduction 5. Specific pollinators (ethological isolation) 6. Different flowering times (allochronic isolation)
Postfertilization	Reduction of zygote formation (prezygotic)	7. Gametic incompatibility*
	Reduction of gene flow through hybrids (postzygotic)	8. Hybrid sterility* 9. Hybrid weakness or breakdown* 10. Lack of hybrid establishment (environmental isolation)

* May be absolute and irreversible.

instances germinate on the style of the supposedly incompatible species; inbreeders and apomicts occasionally outbreed and hybridize; the tail end of the blooming period of one species may overlap with the beginning of the blooming period of a second species; and hybrids germinate and grow in areas where the environment is intermediate between that of the two parental species, even in cases where the hybrids are not very vigorous. As we have seen, once hybrids are established they are capable of crossing with the parental species, leading to the formation of backcrosses and gene exchange between populations.

Because so many plant species are separated by "leaky" isolating barriers and consequently may hybridize, is there not a fallacy in our species concept? In effect, a strict application of the biological species concept to plants will lead to a circumscription of only those taxa that possess absolute barriers to hybridization. This means that many species of oaks would have to be considered as one species, as well as practically all birches and willows, many ferns, orchids, and grasses, and so on. Obviously they are not the same but different species. Consequently, even in cases where no absolute isolating mechanisms are present, new species can be formed and maintained.

Gene Flow and Selection

When considering species formation, selection and gene flow have to be considered in addition to reproductive isolation. Biological phenomena are never undimensional. For ease of understanding, we study them one at a time, but often this can be misleading.

Evolutionarily, the basic unit is the gene pool, which is equated with the local breeding population. But even the concept of the gene pool is an abstraction to a certain extent because it cannot be defined in strict terms. Also as has already been seen in Chapter 4, the breeding mechanism has a great effect on the size and variability of the gene pool. In some outbreeding species, particularly those that have very effective pollinating agents, the gene pool may be rather large; at the other extreme, some populations of apomictic plants may hardly exchange any genes at all generation after generation.

Any mechanism that restricts gene flow may favor speciation. The converse, namely, that speciation will proceed whenever gene flow is restricted, is not true. When two populations are subjected to different selection forces, they

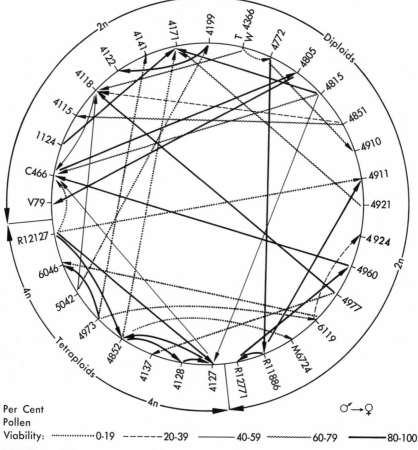

FIG. 7–3. Diagram summarizing average pollen viabilities of progenies obtained from intraspecific hybridizations within and between diploid and tetraploid races of *Lasthenia chrysostoma*. (From Ornduff, 1966, by permission.)

will tend to diverge genetically and thus physiologically and morphologically. Gene exchange will slow down the process of divergence, because intermediate forms will be constantly formed. If selection is not sufficiently great, the formation of two sharply distinct populations is not possible. However, if selection is intense and the intermediate zone very narrow, the formation of two distinct populations can occur and has occurred. Good examples are the evolution of populations adapted to extreme edaphic conditions, such as serpentine and lead, studied by Kruckeberg (1954) and Bradshaw (1959, 1962), already mentioned (page 82).

On the other hand, a number of cases are now known where absolute barriers to gene exchange exist with little or no morphological differentiation. One such case in the *Gilia inconspicua* species group studied by Grant (1964a)

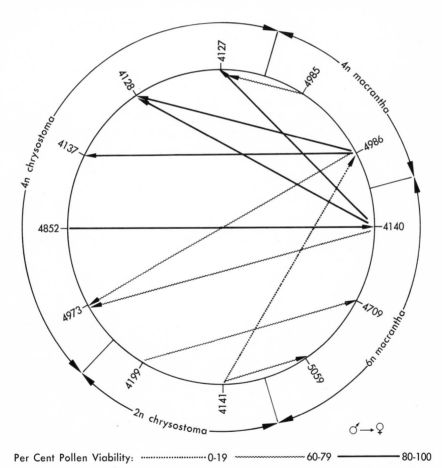

Per Cent Pollen Viability: ·················0-19 ～～～～ 60-79 ————— 80-100

FIG. 7–4. Diagram summarizing average pollen viabilities of progenies obtained from artificial interspecific hybridizations in *Lasthenia*, section *Baeria*. (From Ornduff, 1966, by permission.)

has already been mentioned; another example is *Lasthenia*, belonging to the family Compositae.

In a study of this group of small winter annuals of vernal pools in California, Ornduff (1966) found a composite picture. In section Baeria, for example, *Lasthenia chrysosthoma* was found to have diploid and tetraploid races, while the other species, *L. macrantha*, has diploid and hexaploid races. Crosses between populations of *L. chrysosthoma* with different chromosome numbers yielded hybrids that had reduced pollen fertility, although occasionally the fertility was as high as 50%. However, hybrids between diploid populations also often had reduced fertility, in one instance less than 20% (Fig. 7–3). Crosses within *L. macrantha*, on the other hand, tended to be highly fertile even where the chromosome number differed. Finally, interspecific hybrids were relatively fertile or were sterile, according to the populations crossed and the chromosome number of these populations, but they usually had better than 50% fertility (Fig. 7–4).

We see, then, that there are plant species that are not separated by absolute isolating barriers and, equally important, that there are species whose populations are not entirely interfertile. In addition, the reader should also be reminded that most populations of a species are isolated from other populations because of space and time. Gene exchange between a population of *Glandularia canadensis* from Nashville, Tennessee, and one from Gainsville, Florida, must be very small indeed. Because the probability of direct pollen or seed exchange between the populations is so small as to be almost nil, any exchange is through geographically intermediate populations. Such a process would take at best tens or hundreds of generations. However, as experiments with these plants show, the Nashville, Tennessee, and the Gainsville, Florida, populations have not acquired reproductive isolation, and, although they have differentiated morphologically, the differences are minor.

Species Definition and Classification

How can plant species be defined? The biological species concept defines a species as "a group of interbreeding populations reproductively isolated from any other such group of populations." It has been shown that in too many instances this concept is inapplicable to plants. However, it still remains the only attempt to define a species in nonarbitrary terms—nonarbitrary, because a biological property, interbreeding, is used to define the species. The fact remains, nevertheless, that among plants there is no way of defining species in a nonarbitrary way that will reflect all aspects of the evolutionary situation. If breeding behavior is chosen as the yardstick, many distinct morphological groups can be shown to be interfertile; if morphological similarity is chosen instead, it will soon be apparent that these groups often comprise an assemblage of isolated or partly isolated populations. If physiological and ecological factors are brought to bear, a similar lack of correlation can be observed.

In plants not one but many valid classifications can be made. New statistical methods to be reviewed in Chapter 11 now make it possible to assess degree of relationship in a quantitative fashion. These methods promise, and indeed are already demonstrating, that plants can be classified and their degree of relationship assessed without recourse to subjective evaluation. However, this first classification, this *alpha classification* as it is sometimes called, has to be followed by a study of the breeding mechanisms and the kinds and effectiveness of isolating barriers, both within a species and with other species, and an analysis of the amount of hybridization, if the true biological picture is to be comprehended and the operating evolutionary mechanisms are to be understood.

The enunciation of the biological species concept over a quarter of a century ago was a great advancement in the history of systematics. It pointed out the role of isolating mechanisms and the importance of defining species in a nonarbitrary way. However, in the intervening years much has been learned about population structure and genetics and the mechanisms of speciation. Science, it has been said, is a series of increasingly more accurate approximations to the truth. The species concept reflects this aphorism very well.

Part II

Some Techniques for the Study of Species

Chapter 8

Genetics

Genetics is the science that studies the mechanism of inheritance. Genetics involves many facets, from the investigation of inheritance mechanisms at the molecular and subcellular level (the area known as *molecular genetics*) through the study of the way the genetic code is translated into a phenotype (*developmental genetics*) to the evolution of genetic phenomena in whole populations (*population genetics*). It can be said that no aspect of modern biology is entirely devoid of some genetic implication.

The application of genetic knowledge to evolutionary and systematic questions has produced the biological definition of the species, the modern concept of the breeding population, the various models of selection, and insights into the production and maintenance of variability. However, there is still much room for research. Hardly anything is known about genetic processes in most plants. Those that are best known genetically are some of the cultivated crops, particularly corn, wheat, rye, barley, cotton, tobacco, tomatoes, and potatoes. This knowledge has been derived in great part from efforts at selecting better cultivated varieties. In turn, it has aided immensely in the elucidation of systematic and evolutionary problems in these species as well as adding to the total theoretical knowledge about evolution. These studies have shown very elegantly how a good understanding of the genetics of a species can solve problems of evolution, phylogeny, and classification. Unfortunately, few wild species are as well known genetically as some of our major crops.

Genetic Technique

The basic technique used by the geneticist is the cross. In this respect a modern geneticist proceeds like Mendel did. What has changed is the sophistication with which the progeny is measured and also some of the techniques of producing crosses (Fig. 8–1). For the purpose of this brief discussion we will consider only genetics of higher plants.

In performing a cross the geneticist has in mind a specific theory that he is trying to prove or disprove; this theory relates to the hereditary control of the character he is studying. The theory tells him what proportion of the progeny should be of a specific type, or types. To assure himself that his results are not obtained by chance but are truly representative, the geneticist grows large progenies. Furthermore, in order to minimize environmental variation that may obscure the effect of the genes that he is studying, the geneticist tries to grow his progeny in as uniform an environment as possible as well as use in his plantings special statistical designs that randomize the effect of the environment. Finally, in scoring the progeny, complex statistical analysis is applied to evaluate the results.

Unless these careful approaches are used, no valid genetic conclusions can be drawn. In view of this, how can the biosystematist ever perform meaningful genetic experiments when he is interested not in one character, but in many characters and their inheritance for many populations and species? Will he ever have the necessary time, knowing that every generation will probably take one year to grow to maturity?

Considerations of time and space for growing plants have often prevented the biosystematist from engaging in much meaningful genetic experimentation. As a result, our knowledge about the genetics of natural populations is very meager, incomplete, and tentative. A number of genetic theories concerning the evolution of species have been proposed; few have been conclusively proved or disproved in an experimentally rigorous way.

The biosystematist can use several approaches to circumvent partly the problems of time and space that are posed by the nature of genetic experimentation. First he can take advantage of the natural environment and design experiments involving the manipulation of natural populations. For example, Lewis (1961) in California has set up experimental populations of *Clarkia* in areas where the plants did not grow naturally in order to study the reason for their absence from these areas. Many more such experiments could be performed by biosystematists. They can also take advantage of some striking segregation that is already occurring in natural populations in order to obtain, with only a little further experimentation, an insight into the inheritance of the segregating character. Such experimentation was done by Rollins with *Dithryea wislezenii*, to be explained in detail on page 187.

Through the choice of organisms with short life cycles and small stature, the problems of time and space can be diminished. One such organism introduced in recent years is the small crucifer *Arabidopsis thaliana*, a plant less than eight inches tall that completes its life cycle in a month or less. Finally, the biosystematist can avail himself of certain shortcuts, such as the use of biochemical characteristics, in particular the analysis of proteins and enzymes to be reviewed in Chapter 10.

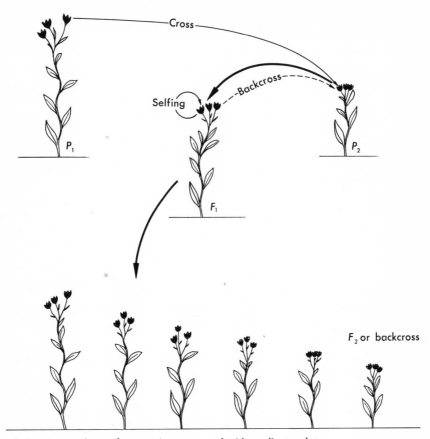

(1) Growing under uniform environment and with replicate plots

(2) Measurements of $\left\{\begin{array}{l}\text{Morphological}\\\text{Ethological}\\\text{Physiological}\\\text{Cytological}\\\text{Chemical}\end{array}\right\}$ Characteristics

(3) Statistical processing

FIG. 8–1. The basic operations performed in any genetical study. Parent plants are crossed, and the hybrid is either selfed, or crossed with a sibling if the hybrid is self-incompatible, to produce an F_2 generation; or otherwise the hybrid is backcrossed to one of its parents to produce a backcross generation. The F_2 or backcross generation is then grown in as uniform an environment as possible, and with replicate plots to nullify the environmental effects on the phenotype. The plants are then studied and measured (for morphological, physiological or biochemical characteristics) and the results treated statistically. The results obtained are then checked with the prediction of how the cross should segregate to see if the hypothesis is upheld or not.

Finally, it is essential whenever genetics is used to explain an evolutionary or systematic phenomenon that it be stated in the form of a hypothesis that can be subjected to experimental test. Otherwise, the explanation, even if plausible, is scientifically meaningless because it cannot be tested.

Genetic Analysis of Characters and of Phenetic Variation

The biosystematist can obtain aid from genetics principally in three areas. The first area is in the analysis of characters. Both in terms of classification and in terms of evolutionary significance, it will make a difference if a character is determined in a simple genetic fashion or in a very complex one, because presumably a character under simple genetic control (one or very few genes) can evolve very quickly and therefore cannot tell us much about the past history of the species that carries it.

The second area in which genetics can be of aid to the biosystematist is in trying to evaluate and assign probabilities to possible phylogenetic pathways. In effect, the effectiveness of selection depends on the heritability of a character, so that an understanding of the mechanisms by which characters are inherited is essential in the evaluation of phylogeny.

Third, and most important, genetics aids the biosystematist in understanding the very foundation of evolution. Evolution is the result of change over time of the frequency of genes in a population. Changes in the frequency of genes are produced by natural selection. That means that interbreeding and its results, which are the domain of the geneticists in their studies, are just as important for the biosystematist. The only difference is one of emphasis: whereas the geneticist will tend to concentrate his attention on the process of hereditary transmission and on the immediate results of a particular cross, the biosystematist is more interested in the overall mechanisms as they affect the population and the species and in the results of several generations of interbreeding. Again, in order to obtain a better understanding of the broad picture, the biosystematist must understand the patterns of character inheritance.

The phenotype is the result of the development of the zygote, which is the first cell of an organism. The transformation of the zygote into a phenotype involves a great number of rather complicated steps, collectively referred to as *development* (Fig. 2–2). The area of development is among the most complicated and least understood of biology. The cytological and biochemical processes of development, however, hold the clue to many of the patterns of inheritance observed when the mature phenotype is studied.

Development consists basically of a series of cell divisions followed by the transformation of most of the cells from undifferentiated, embryonic cells into specialized cells, such as conducting, epidermal, or storage cells. This process of cell division and differentiation is highly coordinated, resulting in the formation of organs such as leaves, roots, and flowers, and in general in the highly stereotyped phenotypic characteristics of each species. Underlying these cellular processes are hundreds and thousands of chemical reactions that by necessity must proceed in a more or less synchronized way.

What accounts for the formation, by most members of a population, of similar phenotypes from undifferentiated zygotes generation after generation? The genes hold the clue to the process of development. The genes are like a set of instructions that determine which biochemical reaction takes place at any one time. In turn, the cellular environment (temperature, pH, presence of minerals, and so on) affect these reactions. The environment of the cell in turn reflects to a certain degree the general environment outside the cell.

A particular phenotypic character is the end result of a large series of cytological and chemical reactions. In some cases, a particular character state is determined by only one gene. In most cases, however, that character state is determined by many genes in rather complicated ways. The geneticist has catalogued the principal patterns of inheritance that have been observed. Because they are essential to an understanding of character inheritance and have biosystematic and evolutionary implications, the principal patterns are described in what follows.

Dominance

Dominance refers to the interaction of two alleles in a heterozygous diploid plant as expressed in the phenotype (Fig. 8–2). The heterozygous plant may be

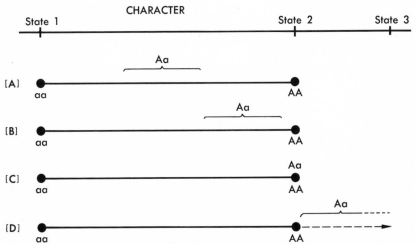

FIG. 8–2. Dominance. The heterozygous phenotype may be (A) Intermediate between the phenotype of the two homozygous parents (codominance); (B) similar to the homozygous dominant parental phenotype but not identical with it (incomplete dominance); (C) indistinguishable from the homozygous parental dominant phenotype (complete dominance); or (D) it may fall outside the variation of the homozygous parental phenotypes (heterosis or over-dominance). The phenotype refers to any characteristic of the plant, be it morphological, physiological, or reproductive.

intermediate between the two homozygous parents (intermediacy or co-dominance), or it may look more like one of the homozygous parents (incomplete dominance), or it may be indistinguishable from it (complete dominance). Finally, it may have characteristics that transcend those of either parent (overdominance or heterosis).

Dominant relations are important in evolution because they allow the storage of genetic variability in the population. Thus, for example, a new, completely recessive gene mutation will not be exposed to selection until it is in the homozygous recessive form. This means that genes can exist in a low frequency in the population as heterozygous recessives without necessarily being of immediate advantage.[1] The same reasoning applies for incompletely dominant genes, except that in these cases the mutant will be exposed to some selection in a heterozygous condition, but this selection may be of less intensity than that against the homozygous recessive.

Epistasis

Epistasis has already been mentioned and briefly discussed in Chapter 4 (page 63). Epistatic interaction exists between two nonallelic genes when one masks the effect of the other so that the phenotype is determined by the former gene and not by the latter when both genes are present in the same genotype. The gene that thus masks or prevents the expression of another is said to be epistatic to it, and the gene that is hidden is said to be hypostatic.

Epistasis can have the same effect on the storage of genetic variability as dominance; that is, it allows the accumulation of genes that if expressed may be negatively selected. An example of epistasis in natural populations is offered by *Viola tricolor* (Clausen, 1926; Clausen and Hiesey, 1958; Grant, 1964b). The normal color of the flowers in this species is violet. There are five genes ($M_1 \cdots M_5$) that affect flower color. The first of these genes (M_1), when present in a dominant form, produces violet flowers regardless of whether the other four genes are in a dominant or recessive form. If, on the other hand, the first gene is present in a double recessive form ($m_1 m_1$), flower color will be light purple whenever the second gene is present in a dominant ($m_1 m_1 M_2 M_2 \cdots$ or $m_1 m_1 M_2 m_2 \cdots$) form, or purple if the first two genes are recessive and the third gene dominant ($m_1 m_1 m_2 m_2 M_3 \cdots$), deep purple if the first three are recessive and the fourth dominant ($m_1 m_1 m_2 m_2 m_3 m_3 M_4 \cdots$), velvety black if the first four are recessive and the fifth dominant ($m_1 m_1 m_2 m_2 m_3 m_3 m_4 m_4 M_5$), and jet black if all five genes are recessive ($m_1 m_1 m_2 m_2 m_3 m_3 m_4 m_4 m_5 m_5$). If we assume that violet flowers have a greater chance of being pollinated by insects, there should be strong selection for plants that are $M_1 M_1 \cdots$ or $M_1 m_1 \cdots$. Selection for the gene M_2 (assuming that light purple is selected over darker shades) can only take place when the

---

[1] The frequency will depend on the mutation rate and the intensity of selection against the homozygous recessive. See Chapter 2 for further details.

plant is $m_1m_1 \cdots$. Since the gene m_1 will presumably be in a low frequency when M_1 is favored over m_1, most plants will be $M_1M_1 \cdots$ or $M_1m_1 \cdots$. Consequently, the other members of the series (M_2, m_2, M_3, and so on) will be protected from adverse selection unless they have other effects on the phenotype (see under pleiotropy). However, if a new and more efficient pollinator were to appear that favors darker shaded flowers, the capacity to produce the darker color is there unhampered by the previous favoritism of the environment for violet-colored flowers.

Pleiotropy

The term *pleiotropy* denotes the occurrence of diverse phenotypic effects by one single gene.

A case of pleiotropy is that of the effect of the gene S in the tobacco plant, *Nicotiana tabacum* (Stebbins, 1959; Grant, 1964b). When the allele S is present in the dominant form it produces leaves with long petioles and acuminate tips, calyces with long slender teeth, corolla lobes with slight tips, long anthers, and elongated capsules. On the other hand, plants homozygous for the recessive allele s have sessile leaves without acuminate tips, calyces with short teeth, corollas without points, short anthers, and roundish capsules.

Pleiotropy, where it has been carefully investigated, is the result of gene action at an early developmental stage, so that not one but many structures are affected. So, for example, the action of the gene S may be to control the type of growth in leaves and flower parts: favoring elongated growth when in the dominant form, hindering it when in the recessive form. Because all genes produce their effect by influencing cellular metabolism, and because it is unlikely that genes exist that manifest themselves only in a single cell, it is likely that most genes are pleiotropic. Detection of the multiple effects of a gene is not easy, however.

From an evolutionary point of view, pleiotropy means that no gene, not even recessive or hypostatic genes, can be truly neutral or completely shielded from selection. Rather, it is a question of degree. The greater the pleiotropic effects of a gene, the larger are its effects on the phenotype so that its exposure to selection is increased. Another effect of pleiotropy is that a gene may produce some effects that are of adaptive value and therefore favorable and others that are less favorable. The gene in question will be selected for or against, depending on its net effect on the phenotype.

Simple and Multiple Factorial Inheritance

The reader is no doubt familiar with Mendel's elegant demonstration (Fig. 8–3) of how a pair of genes controls a phenotypic characteristic such as the flower color or height of the pea plant. Characters that form clear gaps

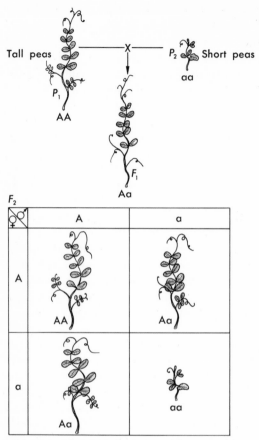

FIG. 8–3. Mendel's crosses with peas. Tall (*AA*) and dwarf (*aa*) peas were crossed, the F_1 (*Aa*) was tall, like the homozygous dominant parent, whereas the F_2 segregated in the well-known 3 : 1 pattern. The two character states, tall and dwarf, were well demarcated, that is, they were qualitative characters, and Mendel did not have to concern himself with the problem that both among the "tall" and the "dwarf" peas, some were slightly taller than others.

between character states so that the difference can be treated as a qualitative one are appropriately called *qualitative characters*.

However, other characters, such as most size differences within a population, form a continuum of variation. In such cases it is difficult, if not impossible, to distinguish discrete groups. Because these characters can be specified accurately only in terms of measurements such as length, weight, or proportion, they are referred to as *quantitative* or *metrical characters*.

Genetically the inheritance of these two kinds of characters is identical. The difference is that qualitative characters are usually controlled by one or, at most, a few genes with very big and often opposite effects, whereas quantitative characters are controlled by many genes with small, additive effects. When many equal genes with additive effects control the variation of a character, the result is ascribed to what is called a *multiple gene system*, *multiple factors*, or *polygenes*.

The existence of multiple factors was first demonstrated by the Swedish geneticist Nilsson-Ehle, who showed (1908) that several genes control the kernel color in wheat. The experiments of Nilsson-Ehle were confirmed by Emerson and East in their studies (1913) on ear size in corn, and conclusively verified by East, who showed (1916) that the difference in flower size in *Nicotiana longiflora* between a long-tubed and a short-tubed variety is controlled by a series of multiple genes with generally similar and cumulative effects (Fig. 8–4).

The essential features of the multiple-factor hypothesis are three: (1) the genes (polygenes) are inherited in a Mendelian fashion, that is, according to Mendelian laws; (2) the genes have effects similar to one another and supplementary to each other; and (3) the effect of each polygene is small in relation to the total variation of the affected character, including the nonheritable component.

Whenever a character is controlled by polygenes, several states or values of that character are possible. Whenever the number of segregating genes is high, let us say over ten, the variation will tend to be continuous, that is, when a population of plants is measured, no discrete classes will be detected (Fig. 8–5). This is because the interaction of the genes creates many classes of character states that are discrete but hard to evaluate and because the environment further blurs the differences between the classes to the point where the observer can no longer detect them. The greater the number of polygenes, the finer are the adjustments the population can make to the environment. So, for example, in the case of *Nicotiana longiflora* mentioned before, the existence of a polygenic system controlling flower tube length allows wild populations to adjust their flower tube length to the insect pollinator that is most prevalent and effective in each locality.

Multiple factor systems probably arise by the accumulation of genes that modify the effect of a major gene until eventually no difference can be established between the original gene and the modifiers.

For the biosystematist trying to assess the evolutionary importance of characters, the difference between qualitative and quantitative characters is an important one. Qualitative characters will be very striking, but their inheritance may be very simple, and therefore they do not necessarily reflect much genetic divergence. On the other hand, if two entities differ by an entire system of polygenes, it reflects a great deal of genetic differentiation, as will be illustrated by the following examples.

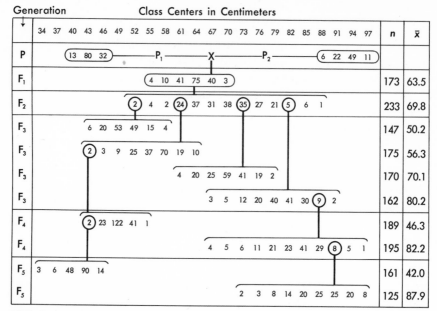

FIG. 8–4. The experiments of East with *Nicotiana longiflora* that demonstrated the multiple factor hypothesis. Plants with short (40–46 cm) and long (88–97 cm) flowers were crossed. The F_1 plants were intermediate (55–70 cm) and the F_2 segregated for this character (52–88 cm). Plants of the F_2 with different values (52, 61, 73, and 82 cm) were selfed. As expected, their progeny segregated, but the values obtained revolved around those of the parent. The same results were obtained in F_4 and F_5. If the variation had been environmental rather than genetic, all generations should have had similar values; if due to one pair of segregating genes, no segregation would have been expected in some lines after the second filial generation. (Numbers in the table refer to number of plants of a certain size, in a certain generation. Note the normal distribution.)

 In 1897 Professor G. Heeger discovered in the market place of Lindau, Germany, on Lake Constance, a few plants of what appeared to be a new species of shepherd's purse, genus *Capsella*, on account of its ellipsoidal capsules instead of the characteristic heart-shaped ones of the common shepherd's purse, *C. bursa-pastoris*. The new form was named by Count Solms-Lambach as *Capsella heegeri* in honor of its discoverer. Because the area in southern Germany where the plant was found was well known botanically, the find attracted quite a lot of attention and was interpreted by the Dutch geneticist Hugo de Vries (one of the rediscoverers of Mendel's laws) as an authentic example of the origin of a new species by saltation or mutation. This was a theory of de Vries' that negated natural selection and attributed the origin of species to mutations of great magnitude.

 The new species was studied by the American geneticist Shull, who crossed it with *C. bursa-pastoris*, the common shepherd's purse. The F_1 of this cross was completely fertile and made up entirely of plants with *bursa-pastoris*-shaped capsules. The F_2 segregated in a ratio of approximately fifteen

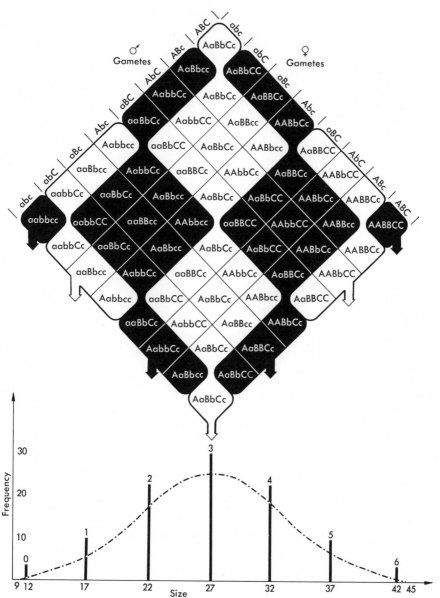

FIG. 8–5. Multiple genes and plasticity combine to produce a continuous (curve) rather than a discontinuous distribution (bar graph). In effect, if we assume that each dominant gene (in the checkerboard) has an effect on size (of a given character x) of 7, and that a recessive gene has an effect of 2, we should obtain seven discrete types measuring 12, 17, 22, 27, 32, 37, and 42 respectively, with a frequency as indicated by the bar graph and corresponding to plants with 0, 1, 2, 3, 4, 5, and 6 dominant genes. However, if the environment has an effect on the plants so that they may deviate by a factor of 3 from the value determined by the genotype, a series of phenotypes will be produced with values ranging continuously from 9 to 45 as shown by the curve. The larger the number of genes involved, the more the distribution will tend to be continuous.

bursa-pastoris to one *heegeri*. This segregation was explained by Shull (1914) as due to the action of two independent genes with similar effects. This conclusion was strengthened by the finding that in the F_3 and F_4 generations certain plants (*CcDD*) segregated in a 3 : 1 ratio, others (*CcDd*) continued in the 15 : 1 ratio, and others (*CCDD*) became constant *bursa-pastoris* or (*ccdd*) *heegeri* (Fig. 8–6). It was clear that in spite of the great morphological differ-

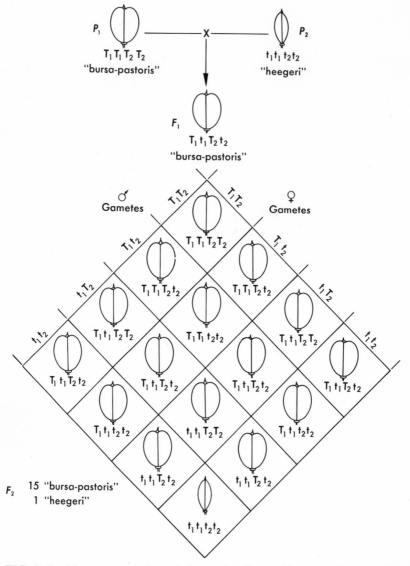

FIG. 8–6. The crosses made and the results obtained by Shull that showed that *C. heegeri* was only a mutant form of *C. bursa-pastoris* and not a new species.

ence in the shape of the silique, *C. heegeri* was nothing but the result of two mutations and not a new species.

Two factors led to this conclusion. First was the fact that the progeny of the *Capsella bursa-pastoris* × *C. heegeri* cross was completely fertile. The second factor was that only two genes were responsible for the difference observed. Both of these criteria are genetic criteria, and the example illustrates very clearly the importance that genetics has acquired in taxonomic studies.

Another interesting although probably unusual example is that of the "almost genus" *Roxira serpentina*. This plant was discovered in 1940 in the inner coast ranges of California near the town of New Idria. It is a little spring-flowering annual, 5 to 15 cm tall, occurring in a small population of some three hundred plants on serpentine soil. The plant belongs to the family Compositae, and its technical characters, particularly the absence of ray flowers, receptacular paleae, and outer involucral bracts, placed it in the tribe (or subtribe) Helenieae. It did not resemble any known genus in that tribe and was thought at first to be a genus new to science. However, its vegetative characters resembled somewhat the genera *Madia* and *Layia* in the subtribe Madineae of the tribe Heliantheae, a tribe closely related to the Helenieae. The resemblances were sufficiently marked for Clausen, Keck, and Hiesey (1947), the discoverers of the plant, to decide to try some artificial crosses. No hybrids were obtained with the species of *Madia*, but vigorous hybrids were obtained in crossings with two *Layia* species (Fig. 8–7). The hybrid with *L. glandulosa* was completely fertile. This is a species of wide distribution in sandy habitats from lower California and Mexico to the state of Washington. The F_1 hybrid had from three to eight rays per head. The F_2 segregated in a complex pattern. It was calculated that at least ten to twenty pairs of genes were possibly involved in the segregations. However, both parental types were recovered in the segregation of the twelve hundred F_2 plants. As a result of this study the plant was described as a subspecies, *L. glandulosa* subspecies *discoidea*, rather than as a new genus.

However, this taxonomic decision was later reversed (Keck, 1958; Munz, 1959) and the subspecies elevated to the rank of species as *Layia discoidea*. The criteria that led to this conclusion were some sterility and hybrid breakdown in some plants of the F_2 and subsequent generations, and also the great morphological dissimilarity between the two parents. This last criterion was reinforced by the knowledge that the genetic difference underlying the morphological difference was quite sizable, too. This is another decision in which genetic criteria were taken strongly into consideration.

Modifiers

According to the classical definition, a modifier gene is one that is not directly concerned with the development of a given character, but nevertheless

FIG. 8–7. (a) *Layia glandulosa* (left) and *Layia discoidea* (right) and their F_1 hybrid. (b) Heads of *Layia glandulosa* (P_1), *Layia discoidea* (P_2), their F_1 hybrid, and twelve F_2 segregants. The rays of the P_1 *Layia glandulosa* can be of two widths (narrow left, broad right), and that character as well as ray number is seen segregating in the F_2. (From Clausen, Keck, and Hiesey, 1947, by permission.)

130

affects or "modifies" the expression of the characters in some manner. Operationally it is often difficult to establish whether a gene is directly concerned with the development of a character, so that usually a gene that affects in a more or less minor way the expression of another gene known to produce a given phenotype effect is called a modifier. An example of a system of modifier genes is the expression of spur length in *Aquilegia* studied by Prazmo.

Most columbines, genus *Aquilegia*, are characterized by petals with long spurs. These spurs are hollow and filled with nectar and attract long-tongued insects, such as butterflies and moths and also hummingbirds. Grant has shown (1952) that the length of the spur is correlated with the length of the tongue or beak of the pollinating insects. So, for example, the spur length of *Aquilegia pubescens* is 3 to 4 cm, whereas the length of the proboscis of its main pollinator, the sphingid moth *Celeria lineata*, is 3 to 4.5 cm (Grant, 1963). Different species of columbines differ in their spur length, and crosses between different species produce hybrids with intermediate spur length and segregating F_2's, indicating that a system of polygenes controls the length of the spur.

Aquilegia ecalcarata is a columbine from China that has no spur. When it is crossed with *A. vulgaris*, a European, spurred columbine, the resulting hybrid has spurs, although of a somewhat reduced size. However, in the F_2, three quarters of the progeny have spurs, and one quarter are spurless (Prazmo, 1960, 1961). When, on the other hand, *A. ecalcarata* is crossed with the North American species *A. chrysantha*, the hybrid also has spurs, but in the F_2 only one sixteenth of the plants are spurless (Table 8–1). This indicates that at least two recessive genes control the spurless conditions, both of which must be present for a plant to be spurless. In the North American *A. chrysantha* the dominant form of both these genes is present, but only one dominant is present in the European columbine species *A. vulgaris*. However, more interesting for our discussion is the fact that the spurred plants of the F_2 of these crosses varied considerably in the length of the spur (Table 8–1). This indicates that the expression of the genes for a spur derived from *A.*

TABLE 8–1

Mean Values and Frequency for Spur Length of the Parents, and First and Second Generation, of a Cross Between *Aquilegia ecalcarata*, Which Is Spurless, and *A. chrysantha*, a Species with Long Spurs. [From Prazmo, 1960.]

Species or Generation	Mean Class Values in Cm																$\overline{\times}$	N
	0	2	5	8	11	14	17	20	23	26	29	32	35	38	41	44		
ecalcarata	20																0	
chrysantha														5	7	8	41.4	20
F_1								5	11	4							22.8	20
F_2	17	35	24	16	20	36	31	34	41	13	12	5					15.2	284

chrysantha are modified by the genetic patrimony of *A. ecalcarata*. Because this last species has no spurs, the genes of this species that modify the expression of the pair of genes that produce a spur in *A. chrysantha* are *modifier genes* by the definition given above. Whether these modifiers in *A. ecalcarata* are homologous with the polygenes that control spur length in the spurred species has not been ascertained. The distinction between modifiers and polygenes may be, however, a semantic and not a biological difference in this case. When in a cross between two spurred species the F_2 segregates for spur length, it is said that the length of the spur is controlled by polygenes. When in a cross between a spurred and a spurless species the F_2 segregates for spur length, it is said that the expression of the genes controlling spur length are modified by the genes of the spurless species. Where is the difference?

The evolution of modifiers shows very clearly the incredibly complicated genetics of a species. Let us briefly review the situation in *Aquilegia*. Spur length is determined by at least two major factors that determine the presence or absence of a spur and a series of modifier genes or polygenes that determine the exact length of the spur. In *A. ecalcarata* modifiers were presumably selected or at least maintained primarily on the basis of their genetic effect on characters other than spur length, that is, on the basis of their pleiotropic action. In turn, the genes that control absence or presence of a spur may act as modifiers of genes that affect other characters. Selection for a spur or for a certain length of spur should therefore also affect other characters of the species, and at the same time the length of the spur is presumably affected by selection for other characters. If dominance and epistasis are also taken into consideration, the incredibly complicated nature of the genetic control of characters should be easily apparent.

Linkage and Crossing-Over

Whenever the parental combinations of genes are recovered in a segregating F_2 population (or a backcross) with a higher frequency than is expected in independent segregation, it is said that those genes are linked. The explanation for linkage lies in the physical fact that linked genes are part of the same chromosome and during meiosis segregate together.

Crossing-over is the genetic phenomenon that results during meiosis in the formation of gametes with novel combinations of genes, that is, the parental genes when there is crossing-over behave as if they were not on the same chromosome. The explanation for crossing-over lies in the as yet not entirely understood phenomenon of chiasma formation during meiotic prophase, at which time chromatids apparently exchange segments. Crossing-over, when it occurs, undoes the effect of linkage and can be considered its counterpart.

The effect of linkage is to influence the frequency by which new combinations of genes are formed in a population. With truly independent segregation of all genes, assortment in the F_2 is complete (usually called *free assortment*), and consequently all combinations should be equally probable. The general effect of linkage is to upset this equality of opportunity and to cause an overabundance of parental combinations and a corresponding deficiency in recombinant types. The magnitude of this effect is related to the recombination value, p, which is the proportion of nonparental types that is recovered in the F_2. So, for example, the number of AB/AB genotypes expected from the selfing of an AB/ab heterozygous plant is given by the formula: $1/4(1 - p)^2$. For a value of $p = 0.01$, 24.50% of the progeny will be AB/AB, whereas with $p = 0.50$, that is, with independent assortment, only 6.25% will be AB/AB. The probability of obtaining a recombinant type, let us say Ab/Ab, is given by the formula: $1/4\,p^2$, and again for a value of $p = 0.01$ would be 0.0025%, that is, only one part in approximately every five thousand, rather than one in approximately twelve, as would be expected with independent assortment. When three or more genes are considered simultaneously, the numerical situation rapidly becomes very complicated. The basic fact, however, remains: the number of new combinations is drastically curtailed as a result of linkage.

Evolutionarily, two aspects of linkage are of importance. First, as already mentioned, linkage tends to hold together existing combinations of genes and therefore can be regarded as a conservative influence, particularly when the population is being subjected to directional selection. Second, if certain neutral or deleterious genes become tightly linked (meaning that they are physically located next to each other or very close so that little or no crossing-over occurs) to genes beneficial to the population, they are protected to a certain extent from selection.

Examples of linkage between favorable and unfavorable genes are known mainly from efforts in plant breeding. One such example cited by Allard (1960) is that of a tight linkage between the genes governing stem rust resistance and late maturity in certain common wheat strains derived from *Triticum timopheevi*. Only after very large populations had been grown and much effort expended were rust-resistant strains with early maturity produced. These plants were those in which crossing-over had occurred. In nature a similar situation favoring early maturity might arise as a result of earlier winters or drier summers, for example. If the climatic change takes place very fast and the populations are small, the population that shows tight linkage might not be able to evolve fast enough because of insufficient crossing-over between the genes, and might become extinct either as a result of lack of resistance to rust or not being able to mature early.

Polymorphism

As the name implies, a polymorphism is the existence of more than one form (referred to as *morphs*) in a population. This may be the existence of flowers

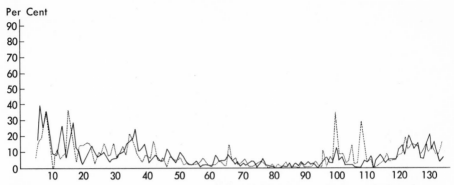

FIG. 8–8. Comparison of mean frequencies of blue-flowered plants during the periods 1944–1947 (solid line) and 1953, 1954, and 1957 (broken line) along a half-mile transect in California. Note how the proportion of blue flowers has remained. remarkably uniform over a thirteen-year period. (From Epling, Lewis, and Ball, 1960.)

of different colors, such as in wild radish (*Raphanus*) and some species of *Leavenworthia* or of *Veronica*. The existence of more than one kind of flower in a heterostylous species would also be considered a polymorphism. Other polymorphisms involve less conspicuous characters. In many plants glabrous and pubescent forms coexist in a population or forms may exist with a pappus or without it, as in *Senecio vulgaris*. Finally, the polymorphism may be strictly cytological or genetical, as in many species of *Oenothera*, where there are two types of chromosomal arrangements.

As has been previously mentioned, according to the theoretical models and also based on direct observation, two types of plants will not be able to coexist with free genetic exchange and without strong selection against the intermediate types, because they will either merge into an intermediate state or one form will be eliminated (Chapter 5). In cases of polymorphism there is presumably free exchange, and the different morphs occur mixed in the population, so there must be some special mechanisms to account for polymorphisms. Let us look at an example.

Linanthus parryae is an annual plant in the family Polemoniaceae, ordinarily 2 to 5 cm tall in nature with a slender stem and branches and small needlelike leaves. It is a conspicuous element of the flora of the Mojave Desert in California, where it is usually the most abundant annual species on the gravelly slopes and alluvial outwashes. It usually produces one to four relatively large white flowers per plant. However, blue-flowered plants are also known. They may occur in all-blue populations, or blue-flowered plants may grow interspersed with white-flowered plants. Experimental studies (Epling and Dobzhansky, 1942) showed that blue is dominant over white. Detailed studies (Epling, Lewis, and Ball, 1960) showed that over a fifteen-year period the frequency of white- and blue-flowered plants over a measured

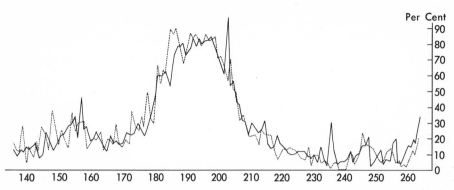

desert transect did not change appreciably, even within a few feet (Fig. 8–8), despite remarkable changes in the density of the populations. Why do these types grow together with so little change? The presence of all-blue-flowered populations as well as the more common all-white populations suggested to Epling, Lewis, and Ball that in some spots there was a definite selective advantage for one of the forms and that the intermediate areas were the result of hybridization. However, their detailed studies also showed that there was very little seed dispersal and that the pollen was, on the average, transported not more than one to ten feet from the mother plant. Consequently, the amount of hybridization in the area where blue and white came into contact could not be very high. If so, selection against either flower color in the mixed areas must also have been very low or there would have been very few such areas. Finally, it was discovered that seed germination was staggered, that is, the seeds produced one year germinated over a number of years, a few at a time. This means that presumably, if a lot of hybrids are produced in a year of high seed production, they will be germinating in that locality for a number of years.

Another interesting polymorphism that exists in many plants involves seedling color. When many species of plants are self-pollinated, it is found that they produce a certain percentage of chlorophyll-deficient seedlings. These seedlings may be completely devoid of chlorophyll (albinos) or show streaks or patches of white in the leaves where chlorophyll has not been formed. Albino plants die under natural conditions once the food source in the seed is exhausted, because they cannot manufacture sugars (however, they can be maintained artificially when grown in an organic medium). In several species that have been studied in some detail, it was found that the chlorophyll deficiency is due to a single recessive gene. A case in point is *Dactylis glomerata* subspecies *judaica*, studied by Apirion and Zohary (1961).

Dactylis glomerata, orchardgrass, is native to the Mediterranean and Middle East regions, where it has formed a number of subspecies. The particular subspecies studied occurs in Israel. It is diploid, self-incompatible, and, of course, cross-fertilized. Among the progeny of these plants occur a certain number of albinos. By means of detailed genetic tests it was estimated that 4% to 30% of the plants in a population may be heterozygous for an albino gene. The average of 14 populations that included 1,163 tested plants was 17%. Heterozygosity was found to be much higher in populations on terra-rosa soil than in those that grow on redzina soil.

The situation in *Dactylis* is not unique, although the number of precise studies is very few. Only corn (*Zea mays*) has been studied in as much detail. However, there are reports for over 150 populations belonging to 7 species (*Lolium perenne, L. multiflorum, Festuca rubra, Phleum pratense, Dactylis glomerata, Trifolium repens,* and *Prunum avium*) and involving collectively several thousand plants that indicate that a mean of 22 plants of every 100 are heterozygous for chlorophyll deficient lethal genes in these species. If all these deficiencies are determined by a single allele and the figure of 22% is at all representative, then the gene frequency for the dominant gene that produces normal chlorophyll is approximately 0.83 and the frequency for the lethal gene approximately 0.11 in these species. A frequency of 11% for a lethal allele in a population would not occur by recurrent mutation alone. There consequently must be a selection in favor of the gene. Because the allele is lethal when homozygous, the selection can only occur in the hetero-zygous state. This is part of the phenomenon of heterosis that was discussed in Chapter 4. Heterosis, then, is also an explanation for the occurrence of natural polymorphisms. In summary, it is clear that there is more than one way of maintaining a polymorphism in a population.

The existence of polymorphisms maintained in a population by heterosis raises an interesting theoretical point, namely, what Haldane has called *genetic death*. If a population has a lethal but heterotic gene with a frequency of 0.1, then in each generation approximately 1% (0.1^2) of homozygous recessive zygotes are produced. These are lethal and will not develop, and the fitness of the population will be reduced. If a second heterotic allele exists with the same frequency, it too will produce 1% of lethals. Of these last some (exactly 1% of them) will be homozygous for both alleles, so that the total population will be reduced by a little under 2% (exactly 1.99%). With ten heterotic genes the populational fitness will be reduced by almost 10%. The failure of zygotes to grow on account of lethal gene combination is referred to as *genetic death*, whereas the phenomenon whereby the popula-tional fitness is reduced because of the presence of lethal genes is referred to as a *genetic load*.

The fact that natural selection will tend to increase fitness in a population has already been discussed. One way of increasing fitness is through an increase in heterotic genes; another by reducing the genetic load. But these two ways work in opposition because an increase in the former means an automatic increase in the latter. There is consequently a limit to the number of heterotic genes that can exist in a population. What exactly this limit is is not very clear yet, but certain calculations seem to set an upper limit of 20% of all genes.

Phenotype, Genotype, Selection, and Evolution

The phenotype is the totality of the characteristics of an organism, that is, the phenotype is the organism's appearance. The genotype, on the other hand, is the totality of all genes of an organism, that is, the genotype is the genetic constitution of an organism. A character is any property of a plant in regard to which similarities or differences between individuals are recordable (Mather, 1949). A great number of characters show heritable variations, including many features of the morphology, anatomy, physiology, cytology, and biochemistry of the plant. Indeed, few geneticists would question the proposition that no character of an organism with the exception of mutilations would fail to show some degree of hereditable variation. However, the magnitude of this variation differs considerably among characters.

The kinds of genes inherited by an organism, that is, the genotype, determine the potentialities for the development of characters, that is, of phenotypes. The environment in which the individual grows and lives determines which of the potentialities will find manifest expression or, in other words, which among the possible phenotypes will eventually be produced.

Variation in characters can be produced in two major ways. First, there can be purely environmental variation. This variation cannot be distinguished from genetic variation by simple inspection, and only a breeding test and/or growing the plants under a controlled uniform environment can tell if a difference observed in the phenotype of two plants is due to the genotype or to the environment, meaning the expression of the genotype in a different environment. Second, variation may be due to changes in the genetic patrimony of the plant. A change in a character can be produced by a change in one or in many genes. Or the change in character may be the result of the expression of a hypostatic gene that normally is not expressed, such as the appearance of a black or purple flower color in a population of pansies; or character change may be due to the fortuitous combination of two or more recessive genes, such as the example of *Capsella heegeri* mentioned earlier. Or the change may be due to a simple segregating gene, as in the case of *Dithrea wislezenii* (page 187). More commonly, the variation is traceable to segregation in multiple gene systems. The only way of telling something about the kind of genetic control of a character is by performing the corresponding crosses and studying the segregation of the offspring.

What is the significance of these many systems of genetic control of characters? It has already been pointed out that, in general, the various types of genic interactions, such as dominance, epistasis, and heterosis, tend to increase the capacity of a population to carry genes that are not expressed, or, in other words, it increases the potential capacity of the population to produce different kinds of phenotypes. The greater this capacity, the greater is its flexibility in case of changes in selection brought about by changing environments. And as was already discussed in Chapter 3, flexibility increases the capacity of the population to exploit the environment and consequently increases its survival potential.

It should also be remembered that in evolution it is always the phenotype as a unit that is being selected. By this we mean that each organism has to be able to reproduce in competition with others and the environment. However, the question of why there is so much diversity in the mechanism of genetic control of phenotypic characters is only partially answered in terms of selection at the level of the population. Biochemical and physicochemical properties of the basic genetic substances, the nucleic acids and proteins, and the way genes are physically put together in a chromosome are just as important. These will be the subject of the next two chapters.

Chapter 9

Cytology

Cytology, the study of the cell, or, more properly, karyology (the study of the cell nucleus), has been an important tool in the elucidation of evolutionary and biosystematic problems. The characteristics of chromosomes and their behavior during cell division and gamete formation (the stages when they can be stained and observed under the microscope) have provided a great deal of relevant information.

The importance of chromosomes is twofold: first, their behavior and characteristics can be used in the classification of species; and second, chromosomes can give an insight into genetic phenomena and the evolutionary processes that lead to the formation of species. Like all characteristics of an organism, chromosomes and the mechanisms of cell division and of gamete formation are subject to natural selection. Therefore, they will vary from species to species as a result of different evolutionary histories. As a rule, this variation is small in related organisms, but can be quite large between distantly related groups. Consequently, the study of cytological differences provides good clues as to the probable evolution of a species.

Three characteristics of chromosomes have the greatest degree of biosystematic information content: (1) chromosome number, (2) chromosome morphology, and (3) chromosome behavior during mitosis and especially meiosis, particularly behavior of the chromosome associations in diakinesis and in metaphase and, to a lesser degree, during the later stages of meiosis. Chromosome number is the easiest information to obtain and to interpret; meiotic behavior, the most difficult. It is not surprising, consequently, to find that our knowledge of chromosome numbers of plants is more satisfactory than our knowledge of the dynamics of cell division.

Cytological Technique

In order that any aspect of the cell may be studied, certain preparatory steps have to be taken (Fig. 9–1). Observations of chromosomes require either living material or specially killed (fixed) material. Herbarium specimens or dried material of any sort is not suitable for chromosome studies.[1]

Direct observations of chromosomes in living material are not performed very frequently. They require special optical equipment, and the observations are often less satisfactory than with fixed material. Until recently, no observations of chromosomes in living material were possible, because chromosomes

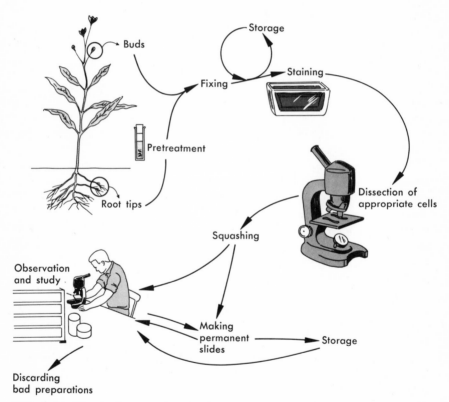

FIG. 9–1. The basic operations performed in any study of chromosomes. If sections are made rather than squashes, a series of steps involving paraffin embedding and sectioning of the appropriate tissues replaces dissection and squashing.

[1] There is apparently one exception, that of the genus *Impatiens*, in which the chromosomes can be counted in pollen grains taken from herbarium specimens. Evidently the chromosomes go into a resting stage at the first mitotic metaphase and stay in that stage until released from the plant (Khoshoo, 1956).

have a density similar to the surrounding karioplasm and are invisible under the light microscope unless they are stained. The light diffraction index of chromosomes is, however, quite different from that of the surrounding medium, and observations of living material were made possible with the development of the phase contrast microscope. The recent introduction of the interference microscope has made observation of living material easier and more precise.

The biosystematist normally fixes his tissues chemically. No chemical or combination of chemicals can fix all the tissues of the cell equally well (see Table 9–1). The normal procedure is to use a fixative that will preserve the

TABLE 9–1

Some Effects on Cytoplasm and Nucleus of Four Common Fixatives.

	Alcohol	Formalin	Acetic Acid	Chromic Acid
Penetration	fast	fast	very fast	slow
Cytoplasm	insoluble precipitate	precipitate	no precipitate	insoluble precipitate
Chromosomes	insoluble precipitate	precipitate (poor fix)	precipitate	insoluble precipitate
Effect on Tissue Volume	great shrinkage	not much change	marked swelling	no change
Hardening	very great	great	very little	moderate

chromosomes and disregard the other cell organelles. As a matter of fact, it is common practice to use one of several alkaloids or chlorinated compounds such as colchicine or paradichlorobenzene as a pretreatment to disrupt the formation of the mitotic spindle. In this way the chromosomes can be spread apart and observed better. In these cases an artifact is produced purposely to observe the chromosome better. Although there is ample justification for these procedures, it should always be kept in mind that the cell and the chromosomes that one observes have been severely modified by the treatments to which they have been exposed.

Not every tissue is suitable for the observation of chromosomes. Since chromosomes can be observed only during cell division, a tissue in active division is a first requirement. Because of optical interference by chloroplasts, green tissues are not as easy to study as colorless ones. Furthermore, on account of location as well as problems of endopolyploidy, secondary meristems are not as satisfactory as are primary meristems. As a result, most studies of mitotic chromosomes are made on the tissues of actively growing root meristems suitably pretreated and fixed. As far as observations of meiosis in angiosperms are concerned, the great majority are made on the microsporocytes, also known as pollen mother cells. This tissue is usually more easily dissected and fixed than embryo mother cells, and pollen mother cells are far more numerous. Meiosis in microsporocytes is also easier to interpret.

A final technical problem is that of sampling. How many observations have to be made before a statement regarding the cytology of an organism can be made? There is no simple answer to this question, but certain guidelines can be given. The first thing to remember is that modifications due to the fixing treatment are more severe in some structures than in others. For example, certain structural details such as primary and secondary constrictions are very much affected by the shrinkage and swelling that accompanies fixing and the flattening process of squashing. Size of chromosomes is also affected, but because presumably all chromosomes in a cell are equally affected, relative size should be less modified than absolute size of the chromosomes. Chromosome number, furthermore, should be the least likely to be affected by fixing of the cellular characters. The number of observations on a given plant should therefore be guided by the types of information being sought. Chromosome number, being easier to estimate, requires fewer good observations than chromosome structure. However, in no case should the chromosome number be determined by a single observation.

Then it should be remembered that any observation is correct at best for a single plant or cell. Any extrapolation to the population or the species entails a guess, qualified by experience, but a guess nevertheless. Ideally, several plants in each population and several populations of a species should be studied before making generalizations for the entire species. Examples of different chromosome numbers within a morphological species are well known: *Cardamine pratensis* (Lövquist, 1958), several species of *Gutierrezia* (Solbrig, 1964), and especially *Claytonia virginiana* (Lewis, W. *et al.*, 1967). Consequently generalizations on single observations should be avoided.

Chromosome Number

Because chromosome number is the easiest to obtain and interpret, by far the largest number of cytological observations have provided this character. Even so, our knowledge of chromosome number in plants is still quite incomplete. For only about 10% of the species of phanerogams is there some knowledge of the chromosome number, and in most of these species only one plant or population has been sampled. For the vascular cryptogams and gymnosperms the percentage is somewhat less, but for the nonvascular cryptogams, particularly the algae and fungi, our knowledge is amazingly poor, mainly because of technical difficulties. In fact, it is very hard to obtain actively dividing tissue in many soil-inhabiting or marine organisms, and, furthermore, the chromosomes of algae and fungi are extremely small and difficult to observe.

Each somatic cell of a flowering plant possesses two sets of homologous chromosomes. Homologous chromosomes are defined as chromosomes that pair completely along their length at meiotic pachytene. At the time of fertilization, the sperm contributes to the zygote a set of chromosomes that is matched one-to-one by a homologous set of chromosomes in the egg. Consequently, the somatic chromosome number of a sexually reproducing plant is an even number. There are exceptions, however, in cases of plants with sex chromosomes, such as in certain liverworts. *Frullania spongiosa* is an example in which the male has eight chromosomes and the female $8 + 1X$ chromosomes (Berrie, 1955). In the flowering plants similar cases have been discussed (page 59). In any event, uneven somatic chromosome numbers are an indication of either an unusual reproductive mechanism or irregular meiosis. It is customary to refer to the somatic chromosome number as "$2n$," and to the gametic one as "n" to emphasize the fact that the somatic number is formed by two sets of homologous chromosomes. Furthermore, the notation x is used when referring to the so-called basic chromosome number in polyploids, as we will see further on.

Chromosome numbers in the vascular plants vary from a low of four somatic chromosomes in *Haplopappus gracilis* (Jackson, 1957) to 1,260 in the fern *Ophioglossum reticulatum* (Ninan, 1958). The great majority of plants, however, appear to have a chromosome number of between 14 and 24 chromosomes (or $n = 7$ to 12).

The changes in chromosome number that can occur during evolution are of two kinds: (1) gain or loss of individual chromosomes due to fragmentation or fusing of the chromosomes without appreciable gain or loss of chromatin (*chromatin*, a name given to the nucleoprotein component of chromosomes visible and stainable under the microscope) and presumably genetic information, and (2) doubling of the chromosome number, generally due to division of the chromosomes without nuclear and cellular division, so that a cell with twice the number of chromosomes is produced. Doubling of chromosome sets is called *polyploidy* (haploid = one set; diploid = two sets; triploid = three sets; tetraploid = four sets; and so on), whereas changes in single chromosomes are called *aneuploidy*.

The distribution of chromosome numbers among the vascular plants is not random. In most genera and families there is a tendency to vary around a mode. Furthermore, in some groups polyploidy is common, in others aneuploidy is often found, and in others there is very little variation of either kind. It is therefore agreed that changes in chromosome number are of evolutionary importance and are related to some kind of selection. However, it is not entirely clear what these controlling factors are. Several plausible hypotheses have been proposed, but they still need to be demonstrated experimentally.

Aneuploidy

Aneuploidy is the change in chromosome number that does not involve doubling of chromosomes. Aneuploid changes usually involve gains or losses of centromeres, but not of chromatin. For example the genus *Brassica* includes species in which $n = 6, 7, 8, 9, 10$, or multiples.

Aneuploid reduction in basic chromosome number was conceived and demonstrated by E. B. Babcock and his associates, particularly H. Tobgy, G. L. Stebbins, and M. S. Walters, in the 1930's and 1940's, working primarily with species of the genus *Crepis*.

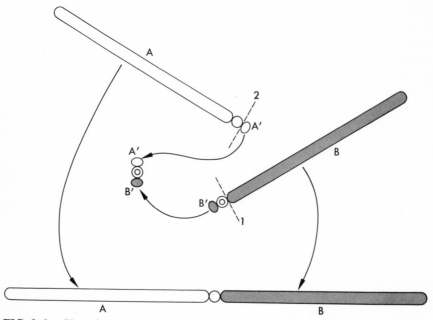

FIG. 9–2. How the chromosome number can be reduced with little or no loss of genetic material by the fusion of two chromosomes—AA′ and BB′—with terminal centromeres to form one chromosome—AB—with one median centromere, and essentially a single centromere with the two short arms A′B′, which can be lost with no genetic effect on the plant. Such a mechanism requires two simultaneous breaks at (1) and (2).

Figure 9–2 illustrates the mechanism that has been proposed to explain the loss of centromeres. Mechanisms for the loss of centromeres are easier to envisage than mechanisms that produce the gain of centromeres, and apparently chromosome reduction is more common than aneuploid chromosome gain. However, experimental evidence is incomplete, and the mechanism depicted in Figure 9–2 is an ingenious interpretation that fits the evidence post facto. For example, Jackson (1962) studying *Haplopappus gracilis* with $n = 2$ determined that it had been derived from *H. ravenii* with $n = 4$ by a mechanism of loss of terminal centromeres and consequent fusion. In other cases, however, changes in chromosome number may involve very drastic rearrangements of the chromosome structure.

An illustration is provided by the studies of Kyhos (1965) with three species of the genus *Chaenactis* (family Compositae) (Fig. 9–3). *Chaenactis glabriuscula* ($n = 6$), *C. fremontii* ($n = 5$), and *C. stevioides* ($n = 5$) are morphologically very similar. One species, *C. glabriuscula*, is common throughout California in mesic areas, the two others being confined to the dry areas of southwest California and adjacent areas in the southwestern United States. By a very careful and detailed analysis of meiosis in interspecific hybrids between these three species, Kyhos showed conclusively that the two species with five pairs of chromosomes have originated independently from six-paired *C. glabriuscula*. In each case, in addition to the loss of the centric region there was extensive repatterning of the chromosome structure involving a series of chromosomal breaks (see Figure 9–3). Similar evidence for extensive chromosome rearrangements was found by Lewis and Roberts (1958) in studying the origin of *Clarkia lingulata* from *Clarkia biloba* (Fig. 9–4).

In these last two cases the simplest explanation for the gain or loss of a centromere illustrated in Figure 9–2 is not correct. If the place where a chromosome break takes place in the chromosome is random, or at least independent from the position of the centromere, then it is to be expected that gains and losses of centromeres will take place in different ways. There is far too little experimental evidence relating to both the mechanisms of chromosome breaks and the manner in which chromosomes are gained or lost.

Polyploidy

Polyploidy is a mechanism that increases the number of chromosomes and, in the angiosperms at least, seems to be much more frequent than the gain or loss of individual centromeres. Polyploidy is important on account of its frequency; about 40% of all flowering plants appear to be of polyploid origin. It is also important as a mechanism of species formation (Chapter 7, page 104).

Basically, there are two kinds of polyploids: allopolyploids (also called amphiploids) and autopolyploids. In an allopolyploid the two sets of chromosomes (from the original diploid) are not homologous; in an autopolyploid they are. The cytological consequence is that in an allotetraploid (Fig. 7–1) there are only two sets of homologous chromosomes, whereas in an autotetraploid there are four sets of homologous chromosomes. Consequently, at meiotic pachytene the chromosomes of each homologous set of an allotetraploid form pairs and produce normal bivalent segregation at metaphase, whereas in an autotetraploid quadrivalents (associations of four homologous chromosomes), form at meiosis, leading to uneven segregation and deficient gametes. Although the concepts of allo- and autopolyploidy are very useful, they are not absolute on account of the difficulty in defining what a homologous chromosome is. In fact, in some cases, such as in the hybrid between

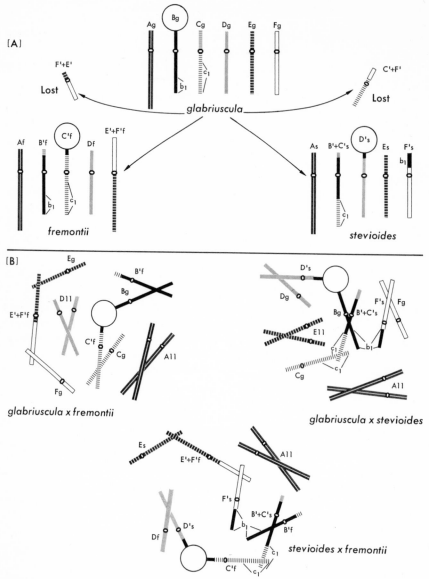

FIG. 9–3. A. A diagram of the probable structural arrangement of the chromosomes of *Chaenactis glabriuscula*, *C. stevioides*, and *C. fremontii*. The approximate positions of the centromeres are indicated by ovals in the chromosomes. The nucleoli are indicated by larger circles attached to the ends of the chromosomes, B. A diagram of the modal pairing configurations at meiosis of the chromosomes in the hybrids between *Chaenactis glabriuscula*, *C. stevioides*, and *C. fremontii*. The maximum configurations occur in the hybrid *C. glabriuscula* × *C. stevioides*. and *C. stevioides* × *C. fremontii* when chiasmata are also formed between the areas designated as b_1. The approximate positions of the centromeres are indicated by ovals in the chromosomes. The nucleoli are indicated by larger circles attached to the ends of the chromosomes. (From Kyhos, 1965, by permission.)

146

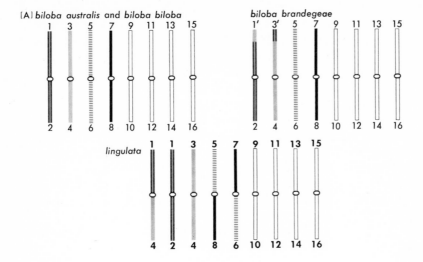

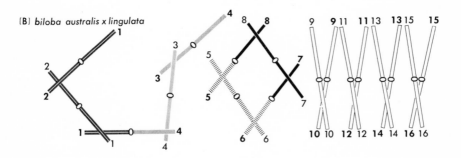

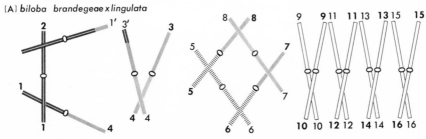

FIG. 9–4. (A) A diagram of the probable structural arrangement of the chromosomes of *Clarkia biloba* subspecies *australis* (genome A), *C. b.* subspecies *biloba* (genome A), *C. b.* subspecies *brandegeae* (genome B), and *C. lingulata* (genome C). (B) A diagram of the modal pairing configurations at meiosis of the chromosomes in the hybrids *Clarkia biloba* subspecies *australis* × *C. lingulata* and *C. b.* subspecies *brandegeae* × *C. lingulata*. An inversion, not shown, differentiates genomes A and B from C, but the chromosome in which the inversion is located is not known. (Modified from Lewis and Roberts, 1956, by permission.)

Glandularia peruviana and *Glandularia pulchella* studied by Schnack and
Solbrig (1953) and mentioned in Chapter 5 (page 75), the chromosomes of
the two species form normal bivalents at meiosis and should be classed as
homologous. However, when an artificial tetraploid was produced experimentally, the chromosomes also formed bivalents (Fig. 9–5). In this case
there seems to be a preferential pairing of chromosomes with their sister
chromosomes in the tetraploid. This situation is one of several referred to as
segmental allopolyploidy (Stebbins, 1947, 1958) and explained as follows.

The two sets of chromosomes (Fig. 9–6) are basically nonhomologous, but
have certain homologous segments. In the diploid hybrid the homologous
segments in the otherwise nonhomologous chromosome pair and produce

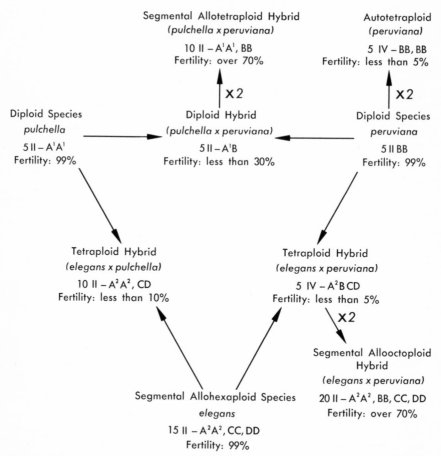

FIG. 9–5. Crosses between two diploid and one hexaploid species of *Glandularia*
and artificial polyploids produced by treating certain plants with colchicine (X2),
their pollen fertility, chromosomal pairing relationships, and inferred genomes.
Note how fertility is restored when a segmental allopolyploid hybrid is produced,
but reduced when an autopolyploid is produced. (From Solbrig *et al.*, 1968.)

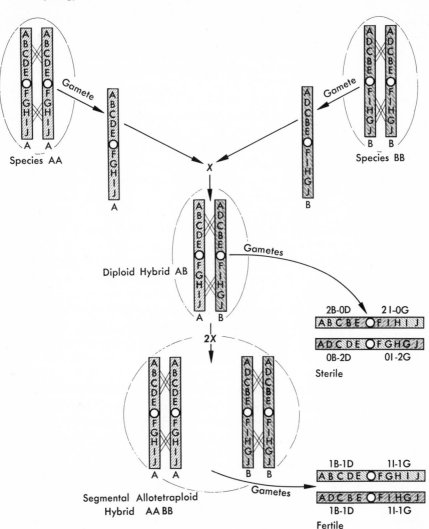

FIG. 9–6. The segmental allopolyploidy theory of Stebbins (1947). The cross between two species, A and B, produces a diploid hybrid with good bivalent pairing, which nevertheless is sterile. This can be explained as owing to small chromosomal inversions, which do not interfere with pairing but lead to duplicated and deficient chromosomal segments in the gametes when cross-over takes place. If the number of chromosomes is doubled, however, pairing takes place preferentially among truly homologous chromosomes (that is those contributed by the same species). Pairing is again bivalent pairing, and the gametes are normal and consequently fertile.

bivalents. However, because the chromosomes are noncomplementary, the resulting gametes will be inviable because of genic deficiencies and duplications (Fig. 9–6). In the tetraploid there are now two chromosomes of each kind that are homologous along their entire length, because they both originated by division from an ancestral chromosome. These truly homologous chromosomes now pair along their entire length and lead to bivalent formation in the tetraploid. A corollary of the segmental allopolyploidy theory is that the loss of fertility of the diploid hybrid should be restored in the tetraploid. In the *Glandularia peruviana* × *G. pulchella* hybrid, the stainability of the pollen with cotton blue (an indication of pollen viability) was increased from approximately 20% in the diploid to over 70% in the artificial segmental allotetraploid. The term *homeologous* has been coined for chromosomes that pair in certain cases (such as diploid hybrids) but are not truly homologous.

Stebbins' hypothesis helps explain cases of polyploidy such as the example just presented. The species of wheat, genus *Triticum*, are a different example of polyploidy.

Species of wheat can be divided into three groups that have 7, 14, and 21 pairs of chromosomes respectively (Sax, 1922). Extensive studies by Sears, Kihara, Stebbins, and others have established that in the hexaploid wheats there are three different sets of seven chromosomes that have been called the A, B, and D genome respectively. The diploid wheats have the A genome. The tetraploid wheats are the result of an ancient hybridization followed by chromosome duplication between diploid wheats and *Aegilops speltoides* or a closely related species that provided the B genome, whereas the hexaploid wheats resulted from the doubling of the chromosome in the hybrid between tetraploid wheat and *Aegilops squarrosa*, a diploid species that furnished the D genome. These hybrids and polyploids have been produced artificially and have been considered always as true allopolyploids, because the chromosomes of the different species will not pair in the hybrids. However, a few years ago Riley and Chapman (1958), studying hybrids between wheat and rye, found some pairing between nonhomologous chromosomes of wheat. A reinvestigation of the problem led to the discovery that in the short arm of chromosome 5B (inherited from *Aegilops speltoides*) of wheat, there is a gene that prevents nonhomologous chromosomes from pairing. If it is removed, multivalent pairing takes place, leading to reduced pollen fertility.

It can be seen, then, that although the concept of allopolyploidy, segmental allopolyploidy, and autopolyploidy are useful operational concepts, the absolute degree of homology between the chromosomes of two species cannot be judged with certainty from their degree of pairing alone. Furthermore, an explanation of meiotic pairing based only on degree of homology of chromosomal segments may be too simplistic. This is an area in need of much more study.

The mechanism of allopolyploidy and of segmental allopolyploidy allows a kind of instant speciation, as was already mentioned in Chapter 7. In effect, the polyploid hybrid will combine the characteristics of the two parental species and at the same time will be partly genetically isolated, because the backcross hybrids will show a certain degree of sterility. However, some other factors are needed for the polyploid to become established. First, there must be a suitable environment, and secondly, the new form has to migrate into a new territory or it will be swamped by diploid pollen of the parental species, leading to the formation of a progeny of partially or totally sterile triploids.

The evolutionary role and frequency of autopolyploidy is harder to assess. Until recently it was believed that most natural polyploidy was allopolyploidy or segmental allopolyploidy. This belief was based largely on the fact that a true autopolyploid shows tetravalent (associations of four chromosomes) pairing at meiosis on account of the presence of four homologous chromosomes and shows, consequently, a great reduction in fertility. Recently, however, a number of cases of polyploids that are morphologically identical to diploids have been studied, leading to the hypothesis that they are autopolyploids. One such case, already mentioned before, is the study of natural populations of *Gutierrezia sarothrae* (Solbrig, 1964). Ten out of fifty-three populations studied were tetraploid, the other forty-three diploid (Fig. 9–7).

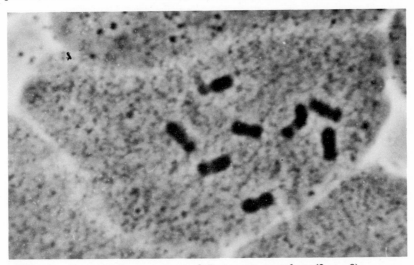

FIG. 9–7.   Somatic chromosomes of *Gutierrezia sarothrae* ($2n = 8$).

The diploids could be differentiated from the tetraploids in only one (pollen diameter) of eleven characters studied. The only possible explanation with the evidence at hand is that the tetraploids are the result of autotetraploidy, in spite of the normal formation of bivalents instead of quadrivalents at meiosis. Autopolyploidy may be more frequent in nature than has been assumed so far. Only more and better sampling of chromosome numbers in plant populations and detailed study of populations with different chromosome numbers can tell.

In summary, chromosome number is an important characteristic because it can help delimit gene pools. Knowing the chromosome number can often tell us something about phylogeny, because the probability is very small that a diploid may have been derived from a polyploid (see, however, Raven and Thompson, 1964, for a different opinion). It is particularly useful within a species to trace evolutionary changes. However, caution should be exercised not to draw conclusions based exclusively on chromosome numbers without the corresponding data on chromosome homologies.

Chromosome Morphology

The chromosomes are nuclear organelles stainable and visible under the light microscope during cell division. They are elongate in shape, with a constriction called the *centromere* somewhere along their length. The centromere divides the chromosome into two parts called chromosomal arms. The centromere plays an important role in the movement of the chromosomes to the poles during cell division, although exactly how it works is not yet fully understood. The position of the centromeres can vary from chromosome to chromosome so that the two chromosomal arms will be of equal length when the centromere is in the center of the chromosome or of unequal lengths when the centromere is nearer to one end of the chromosome than the other. This provides a means of classifying the chromosomes into types: (1) median, when the centromere is in the center and the arms are essentially of the same length; (2) submedian, when the centromere is nearer the center and the arms are dissimilar in length but not extremely so; (3) subterminal, when the centromere is nearer to one end; and (4) terminal, when the centromere is at the very end and there is only one arm (a rare, but not unknown, situation). Categories two and three are often lumped under the general term *acrocentric*. Since the centromere can occupy any position along the chromosome, these chromosomal types are somewhat subjective.

A second way to identify chromosomes is by their length. The length of the chromosomes varies from about one micron to 30 microns, with most chromosomes being less than 10 microns in length during the stage of maximum contraction in mitosis. Absolute length of the chromosome and relative length of the two chromosomal arms are the main and often the only ways of recognizing individual chromosomes in a cell. However, it should be remembered that during the early stages of cell division the chromosomes are becoming shorter; after metaphase this is reversed and they enlarge. Any measurement aimed at comparing absolute lengths of the chromosomes of different organisms should always be made at exactly the same stage of cell division, preferably at the stage of maximum contraction at metaphase. It also should be remembered that the usual pretreatments, as well as some of the fixatives commonly employed, particularly acetic acid, have a marked effect on chromosome length (they shorten the chromosomes). It is consequently far more precise for purposes of comparison to express the length of a chromosome as a proportion of the total length of the genome (obtained by dividing the absolute length of the chromosome under investigation by the sum of the lengths of all the chromosomes in the genome).

Sometimes chromosomes can be identified by additional characteristics. One frequently used is the possession at one end of a small, usually rounded body called a *satellite*, which is united to the main body of the chromosome by a thin, threadlike filament called a secondary constriction. The chromosome with the satellite is called an *SAT chromosome*.[2] Usually only one pair of homologous chromosomes possesses satellites. An individual chromosome does not have more than one satellite. Another characteristic by which chromosomes can sometimes be distinguished is the presence of distinct areas of strongly stainable material called *heterochromatin*. These areas can be best observed during mitotic prophase, but because this stage usually is comparatively difficult to study, heterochromatic areas are not commonly very useful in identifying chromosomes.

Chromosome morphology can be used for purposes of species identification and classification as well as for purposes of phylogenetic interpretation. Differences in the karyotype of two organisms can be treated similarly to differences in chromosome number. However, because data on chromosome structure are more difficult to obtain and the probability that they reflect an isolation barrier is not as high as with chromosome number, they are used infrequently for this purpose.

Changes in the morphology of the chromosome are a reflection of internal rearrangements of the chromosomes. These changes are collectively referred to as *chromosomal aberrations*. Figure 9–8 shows the kinds of aberrations that can occur. The effect on the shape and relative size of the chromosomes will depend on the size of the chromosomal segment involved in the aberration and the kind of aberration. A paracentric inversion never affects size of the chromosome or the position of the centromere: it may have an effect on the position of secondary constrictions and heterochromatic segments. Deletions and duplications usually involve very small chromosomal segments and consequently it is unlikely that they can be discovered by cytological means. Pericentric inversions affect the position of the centromere in the chromosome with the exception of the case when the two breaks occur equidistally from the centromere. Shifts will affect the centromere whenever it is included in the shifted segment. Finally, translocations affect the size of two chromosomes as well as the relative position of their centromeres whenever the translocated segments are of unequal length.

However, as can be seen in Figure 9–9, chromosomal aberrations can be determined more precisely in meiosis of a plant heterozygous for the aberration. Most such aberrations are detected as a result of intra- or interspecific hybridizations. Nevertheless, sometimes the plants involved are distantly related so that artificial hybrids are not viable. In such cases a study of

---

[2] Not an abbreviation of satellite, but because at one time it was thought that it lacked DNA: *Sine Acido Thimonucleico* (Acido Thimonucleico = DNA).

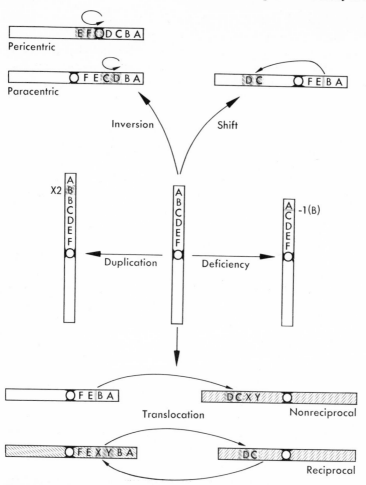

FIG. 9–8. The various kinds of chromosomal aberrations and how they can affect the morphology of the chromosomes. The size of the segment that is involved determines the magnitude of the change.

chromosome morphology can be revealing. A case in point is the pair of species *Gutierrezia sarothrae* and *G. texana*. Both these species have four pairs of chromosomes. The former is a shrub whereas the latter is a stout annual. Their ranges overlap in Texas and New Mexico, but no hybrids are formed. Nor could hybrids be obtained when artificial crossing was attempted. A study of the morphology of their chromosomes was undertaken to see if they were different (Rüdenberg and Solbrig, 1963). *Gutierrezia sarothrae* (as well as all the other perennial species studied) has a karyotype that consists of one metacentric and three acrocentric chromosomes. The short arm in one of the acrocentric pairs is considerably longer than in the other two, and of these last two one possesses a satellite. All four chromosomes can therefore

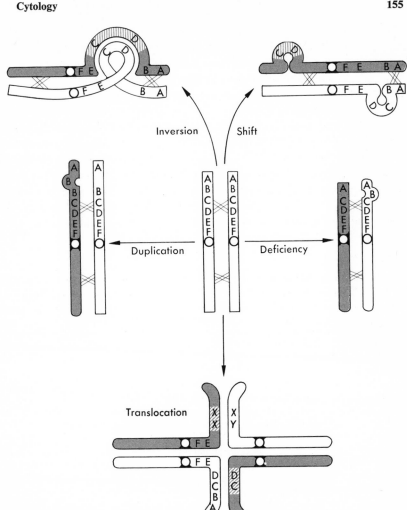

FIG. 9–9. How the various chromosomal aberrations affect pairing of chromosomes at meiosis when in a heterozygous condition.

be identified by structure alone. In addition there is a relative size difference among the four chromosomes: the SAT chromosome is the longest, followed by the subterminal, the submedian, and the median in that order (Fig. 9–7). *Gutierrezia texana* also has four pairs of chromosomes, but they show a different structure. There is also one median and three acrocentric chromosomes, but the median is clearly the largest chromosome. Of the three acrocentric ones, two are subterminal and one submedian. A minimum of two translocations is needed to explain the differences between the morphology of the chromosomes of the annual and perennial species of *Gutierrezia* (Fig. 9–7).

In summary, the study of chromosomal morphology is generally not a very powerful tool for interpretation of variability. Chromosomal differences per se do not indicate crossability barriers, and they cannot be used to establish phylogenetic differences in any firm way. They provide additional data in the cases where hybrids are known, and they may be of use for classificatory purposes.

Detailed studies of chromosome structure can, however, be of importance for detecting broad phylogenetic affinities in certain cases. A good example is the family Onagraceae. The unusual diversity of chromosome number and morphology (Kurabayashi, et al., 1962) found in Onagraceae has proved useful in determining a generic classification (Raven, 1964). In fact, each of the six tribes into which the family Onagraceae is divided can in some degree be characterized chromosomally (Table 9–2). Added to an under-

TABLE 9–2

Chromosomal Characteristics of Members of the Family Onagraceae That Are of Use in the Delimitation of the Tribes of the Family. (Data from Kurabayashi et al., 1962.)

Tribes	Chromosomal Characteristics
Fuchsieae Lopezieae Circaeae	No definite interphase chromocenters; contraction of chromosomes even along a gradient during prophase; in some species many chromosomes acrocentric.
Epilobieae Jussiaeae	Definite interphase chromocenters; contraction not along a gradient; chromosomes within a genome heterogeneous in size and proportion of differentiated segments.
Onagreae*	Translocation systems; definite interphase chromocenters; contraction not along a gradient; most chromosomes metacentric, subequal in size, uniformly differentiated.

* Tribe Hauyeae has been incorporated into Onagreae (Raven, 1964).

standing of the morphology and geography of the genera that is rivaled by few other families, the phenetic affinities and the presumed phylogenetic relationships of the genera can be determined quite accurately.

Meiotic Phenomena

The study of the process of meiosis and of gametic formation in a normal plant is of considerable importance in understanding the processes of genetic transmission from generation to generation. However, for the biosystematist the study of meiosis in hybrids, where it is likely to be irregular, is of still more interest, because it can provide evolutionary information. The observed irregularities are interpreted as a sign of disharmony between the genetic systems[3] of the individuals.

In order to understand and interpret irregular meiosis, the process in normal individuals has to be well understood. Unfortunately, there are still aspects of meiosis that have escaped the scrutinizing eye of science. The two most important of these aspects are (1) the pairing mechanism itself, and (2) the process of chiasma formation and genetic crossing-over.

Let us analyze how a study of meiosis in hybrids can be used to obtain biosystematic information.

A measure of species relationship that has been used very extensively by biosystematists is the fertility of interspecific hybrids measured either in terms of their ability to set seed or the percentage of viable gametes (usually estimated by the number of viable pollen grains) that they are able to form.

When a normal, vigorous hybrid is formed, hybrid fertility depends on several factors. An important one is the degree of homology between the chromosomes of the two species. In effect, as a result of crossing-over and of independent assortment of the chromosomes at meiosis, the gametes of the hybrid are formed by a mixture of chromosomes and chromosome segments of the two species. If these chromosomes are not interchangeable, either because their genetic message contained in the DNA is no longer compatible or because the corresponding genetic message has been transferred to another chromosome as a result of chromosomal aberrations, gamete sterility will result. The greater the number of nonhomologous segments, the greater the degree of sterility.

In principle, the degree of gamete sterility furnishes an ideal method for assessing the genetic relationship between two species. The only problem is that some or all of the sterility may be due to chromosomal aberrations rather than genetic differentiation. Cytologically it is possible to identify major chromosomal aberrations, but it is impossible to tell minor ones (cryptic aberrations) from mutations. Furthermore, it is clear that mutations that produce morphological changes do not necessarily affect pairing. A case in point is presented by some crosses in the genus *Glandularia* that were briefly discussed in Chapter 5 (page 75). The three species *G. peruviana*, *G. pulchella*, and *G. santiaguensis* occupy approximately the same habitat of open, dry, and semidry grassland in northern and central Argentina. Morphologically, *G. peruviana* differs from the other species because of its entire leaves, more appressed habit, larger internodes, large red flowers, and absence of glandular appendages. *Glandularia santiaguensis*, in turn, is a taller plant than *G. pulchella*, with larger leaves and flowers and less divided leaves (Fig. 5–1). Hybrids between *G. santiaguensis* and *G. peruviana* are 50% pollen sterile (Solbrig, 1968). The reduced sterility is due to at least one translocation

---

[3] *Genetic system*: the totality of the hereditary mechanisms controlling variability, encompassing such matters as the number of chromosomes, degree of crossing-over, the breeding system, and so on. See Chapter 4, page 49.

and probably also to small cryptic aberrations, because the chiasma frequency of the hybrid is lower than that of the parent, leading to the formation of approximately 4% of univalents (although the reduced chiasma frequency could, of course, also be due just to the effect of the translocation or to some specific mutation). Very similar cytological behavior was found by Schnack and Covas (1945) in a hybrid between *G. santiaguensis* and *G. pulchella*. The cross between *G. peruviana* and *G. pulchella*, on the other hand, was 42% pollen fertile, but in spite of this showed almost normal meiotic pairing. The differences are almost entirely due to small cryptic aberrations, as shown by the fact that the artificial allopolyploid had a pollen fertility of over 70% (Schnack and Solbrig, 1953). On morphological grounds, *G. santiaguensis* and *G. pulchella* are more related to each other than to *G. peruviana*; chromosomally, however, *G. pulchella* and *G. peruviana* appear to be closer, although the genetic isolating barrier between all three species is about the same. It is evident that in this case morphological differentiation (and the genetic system underlying it) has developed at different rates in the three species than have the genetic and cytological factors producing reduced fertility in the hybrid.

Analysis of meiosis can tell us much about the mechanisms producing sterility in hybrids. However, as a general and absolute measure of relationship such an analysis is weak because of incomplete knowledge about the mechanism of meiosis itself and because the correlation between genetic changes and chromosomal changes is not absolute.

Summary and Conclusions

In summary, the importance of the role that cytogenetics has played and still plays in biosystematic studies should be affirmed once more. It should, however, be emphasized that it is not the answer to all biosystematic problems. In part, this is because at present there is a lack of understanding of some basic cytological phenomena, such as most causal aspects of meiosis. Also, there are not, at present, adequate techniques to measure with precision the degree of pairing and chiasma formation. However, even if all these problems could be answered (as they will be some day), cytology still could not produce all the answers to the genetic and evolutionary questions posed by the biosystematist. This is because real comprehension of most biological phenomena must include physicochemical information. Let us then see to what extent chemical approaches have been developed in biosystematics.

Chapter 10

Chemistry

In the last analysis, many biological phenomena can be broken down into simple physicochemical reactions, each being highly deterministic and following rigidly the laws of thermodynamic equilibrium. However, it would be an error to consider biology as simple, because what makes organisms so tremendously complex and varied are not the principles controlling a single reaction, but the combination and interaction and distribution in time and space of thousands or millions of basically simple reactions. And, when the number of variables that affect a particular reaction becomes large, the outcome can be partly stochastic and not wholly deterministic.

As can be easily imagined, the study of all the chemical reactions taking place in a cell throughout the life of an organism is a gargantuan task. It has, however, the attraction provided by the knowledge that this complexity may be broken down into simple physicochemical interactions. It is a task requiring great imagination, technical skill, and specialized equipment. It is no wonder that it has lured more biologists, biochemists, and even physicists than any other aspect of biology. There are more scientists working on biochemistry, molecular biology, cell biology, and developmental biology today than all systematists of all times put together. And this combined attack is yielding a tremendous amount of very detailed information. Much of it is trivial and/or highly specialized, some of it includes the greatest discoveries made by man, for example, the discovery of the role of DNA in genetic transmission (Avery, MacLeod, and McCarthy, 1944), the elucidation of the physical structure of DNA (Watson and Crick, 1953), the breaking of the genetic code (Nirenberg and Matthaei, 1961; Nirenberg *et al.*, 1963), and the elucidation of the facts of protein synthesis and the role of enzymes in development.

Eventually, enough will be known to afford a better understanding of the way an organism functions. It will be immediately apparent that this information is exactly what the biosystematist needs and wants in order to understand the interrelationships of organisms, populations, and species. Although the chemical characteristics of organisms have been used from the very beginning of scientific taxonomy (color of flowers, characteristic smells of certain species, peculiar tastes of leaves, and so on), it has only been for about one hundred years that an attempt has been made at the identification of these substances. Natural product chemistry, as this field has come to be known, has made great strides in the last century. The major plant constituents have been isolated and their chemical structures identified. Many have been synthesized in the laboratory, and in many cases their biosynthesis has also been learned. Natural products chemistry has developed, however, largely independently from systematics, as a subdiscipline of chemistry rather than of biology. This is in part because until recently there was no general biological theory to which these chemical data could be fitted. In the last twenty years discoveries in the field of molecular biology and molecular genetics have provided the needed theoretical framework. Chemical systematics, that is, the use of chemical data of all sorts in systematic investigations, has blossomed and is now a recognized and very active area of systematics. Let us now turn to some of the problems associated with this new field.

Chemical Techniques

The study of chemical characteristics requires a more sophisticated methodology than the study of morphology, gross anatomy, or even cytology. Chemical compounds cannot be observed in the ordinary way that a morphological structure is observed; neither can they be fixed and preserved in the manner of tissue sections or chromosomes. What are studied are properties associated with a certain class of compounds and from these properties the presence of the compound or compounds is inferred. The properties that are most commonly studied are the relative solubilities in various kinds of solvents, reactivities with specific compounds, and optical and electrical properties.

Plant tissues are a complex mixture of chemical substances. A first step in the study of these substances is the separation and purification of the compound under study from this mixture. The method varies with the kind of substances to be separated. But usually a first step consists of extraction with some appropriate solvent followed by chromatographic or electrophoretic separation. These last two methods have come into existence in the last twenty years, and they have greatly simplified the task of separating natural products so that it is now possible to sample routinely relatively large populations for the presence of a compound. These new methods also permit analyzing samples formed by smaller quantities. A last step is the chemical identification of the various compounds that have been extracted and separated. (Fig. 10–1).

A first approximation to the identity of the compound or to the chemical family to which it belongs can be obtained by colorimetric procedures or by

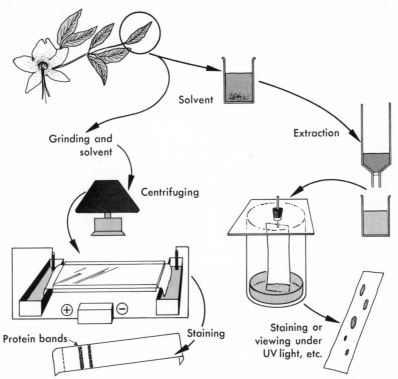

FIG. 10–1. Some of the operations performed in separating chemical substances for biosystematic purposes through electrophoresis and paper chromatography, two common techniques used in the study of proteins and flavonoid pigments, respectively.

the use of staining methods. Often these procedures are sufficient if it is already known from a previous identification that the particular compound is found in the plant. However, precise chemical identification usually requires specialized chemical knowledge, particularly if the compound is new to science or if a precise structural determination is wanted. When the investigation moves into this area, collaboration with a trained chemist becomes necessary.

A further technical point that has to be remembered is that under aberrant circumstances chemical substances can interact with each other to give rise to new compounds or break down into simpler substances unless extreme care is taken to avoid it. In each of these cases, artifacts are produced. It is very important, therefore, to repeat experiments carefully several times to be absolutely certain of the reproducibility of the results.

The biosystematist working in biochemical systematics has to have some chemical training. However, there is ample latitude in the depth of training required, and investigations can be done with very simple methodology requiring only a superficial acquaintance with modern chemistry, or they can be very thorough, involving a team of biochemists and considerable equipment. Obviously, many fine points will escape if the investigation is stopped after the first routine survey, but some important knowledge will be gained. The important thing is not to make biosystematic or chemical conclusions inconsistent with the data at hand.

Chemical Approaches to Biosystematics

The classes of chemical compounds that can be and are used for taxonomic and evolutionary purposes are legion. They can be classed into three major categories: primary and secondary plant metabolites, primary gene products, and nucleic acids. Primary plant products are those compounds that the cell elaborates and that are basic for its metabolism: sugars of many kinds, carbohydrate polymers such as starch and cellulose, lipids of many kinds, compounds such as ATP and DPN that are involved in the transfer of energy-rich bonds and oxi-reductions, storage proteins of many sorts, and so on. Secondary plant products are those compounds whose function is not always very well understood, but that do not seem to be essential, because they are not universally present in all plants (they are likely to be essential to the plant that produces them). They comprise such compounds as alkaloids, the anthocyanin and flavonoid pigments, resins of different sorts, and so on.

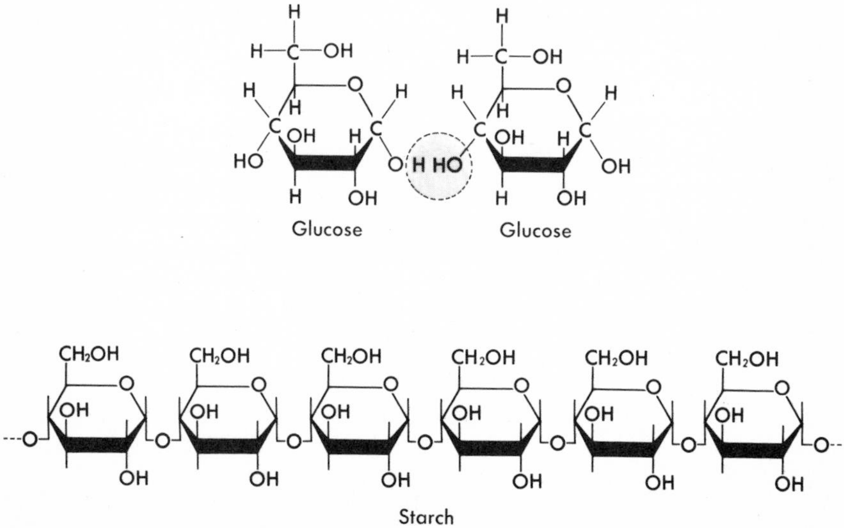

FIG. 10–2. The structure of starch. Note that it is a very simple polymer, the repeating unit being a molecule of glucose. Contrast with DNA (Fig. 10–3) and a protein (Fig. 10–5), which are also polymers.

It is not always easy to make a distinction between primary and secondary metabolites, and the division is primarily one of convenience.

Primary gene products are the enzymes and proteins that are produced directly as a result of the reading of the genetic message contained in the chromosomal DNA. While primary and secondary metabolites are highly varied from the chemical point of view, all enzymes are proteins, being chains of different mixtures of twenty amino acid residues. However whereas primary and secondary metabolites tend to be compounds of low molecular weight, or if they are large molecules they are usually polymers that repeat a simple unit (Fig. 10–2), enzymes are compounds of high molecular weight (usually 500,000 or more, although some, such as ribonucleoase, have a molecular weight of only 13,000).

Finally, the nucleic acids are two, DNA and RNA. In the higher plants the genetic message is carried in the DNA of the chromosomes. The chemical

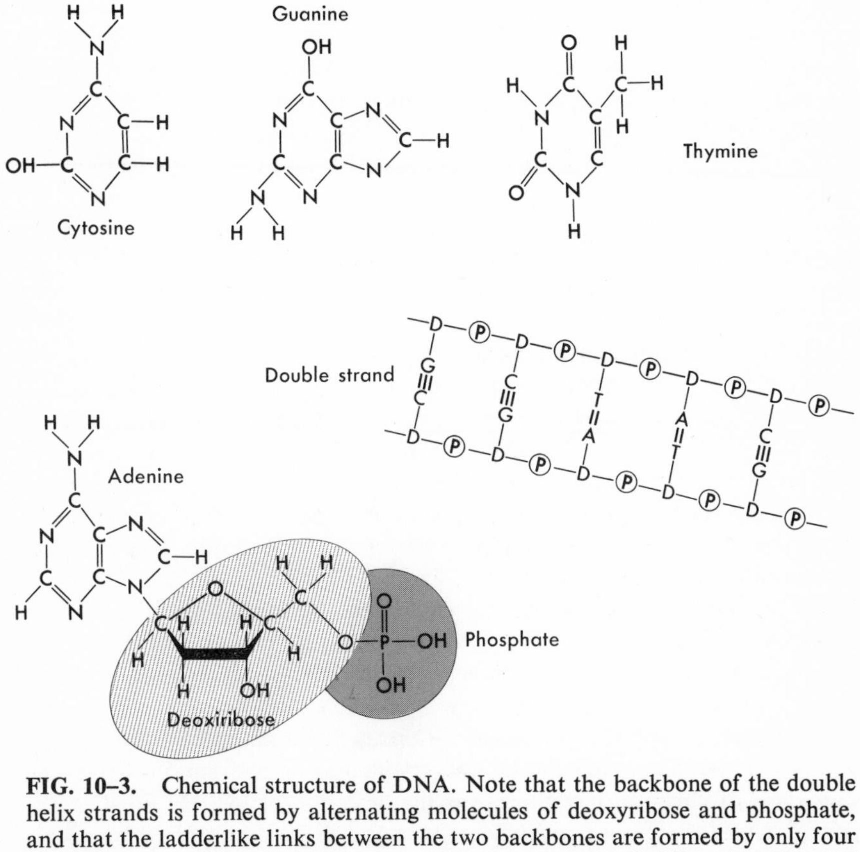

FIG. 10–3. Chemical structure of DNA. Note that the backbone of the double helix strands is formed by alternating molecules of deoxyribose and phosphate, and that the ladderlike links between the two backbones are formed by only four molecules: two purines (adenine and cytosine) and two pyrimidines (guanine and thymine).

structure of DNA is relatively simple. It is also a polymer with a relatively simple basic unit. However, its biological function is partly due to its chemical as well as its physical structure (Fig. 10–3). Each of these three major kinds of compounds furnishes different kinds of information to the biosystematist.

Primary and Secondary Metabolites

The primary metabolites tend to be of universal occurrence. The basic functions of the plant, such as respiration and photosynthesis (to name two that are fairly well understood), are relatively uniform throughout the plant kingdom. Any change in these processes as a result of mutation must be of immediate advantage or the total efficiency of the plant is impaired. Because of this greater uniformity, primary metabolites show much less variation within species and between related species.

Secondary metabolites, on the other hand, are quite variable. Most of them are not of universal occurrence and consequently can be used to characterize taxa at various levels. Algal classes have been characterized by their pigments from the early days of algal systematics. The presence and kinds of porphyrins (cytochromes, chlorophylls, phycobilins) and carotenoids have been used as the major key characters. Other compounds are restricted to a still smaller group, such as the betalins (nitrogenous anthocyanins), which occur only in the families of the order Centrospermae with the exception of the Caryophyllaceae.

However, important as chemical characters may on occasion be as identifying characters in the circumscription of a group of plants, they are no more useful than morphological characters or any other characters for this purpose. The difficulties associated with their identification often make them less useful. They are, however, important in other ways.

One of the most important applications of biochemical systematics has been in the detection and measurement of hybridization and introgression. Although F_1 hybrids can usually be detected by morphological characters alone, it is much more difficult to detect backcrosses. Because the amount of backcrossing may be of more consequence in evolution than the number of F_1 hybrids, this inability to estimate accurately the degree of backcrossing has hampered the documentation of specific cases of hybridization.

Alston and Turner have studied extensively hybridization in the genus *Baptisia*, a genus formed by twenty species of shrubs common in the central and eastern part of the United States. Whenever two species grow together they usually hybridize, provided they bloom at about the same time of the year. However, there are great fluctuations in the amount of hybridization and introgression in each situation. A very interesting case that illustrates the usefulness of chemical techniques for the detection of hybrids involves the pair of hybrids between *Baptisia lanceolata* and *B. pendula*, and *B. lanceolata* and *B. alba*. The two species *B. pendula* and *B. alba* are both white-flowered and are morphologically rather similar. They are distinguished from each other with difficulty by their fruit characters. They can, however, be recognized by their distinct flavonoids.

In 1961 Alston and collaborators (Alston, *et al.*, 1962) collected in Georgia a hybrid population that was tentatively identified on morphological grounds as *B. lanceolata* × *B. pendula*. Both of the putative parents were observed in the area. However, when the flavonoids of this hybrid were analyzed, the chromatographic analysis indicated that it was a hybrid between *B. lanceolata* and *B. alba*. Field studies the following year produced in the vicinity the *B. alba* parent, which had not been detected previously. At that time another hybrid population was discovered, morphologically indistinguishable from the one discovered the previous year. However, analysis of the flavonoids indicated that the second hybrid was the *B. lanceolata* × *B. pendula* hybrid that could not be found the previous year. On morphological grounds the two sets of hybrids are indistinguishable; chemically, however, they can be identified relatively easily.

Another interesting situation in which chromatographic techniques proved to be much more discriminating than morphology involves four other species of *Baptisia* (*B. leucophaea*, *B. sphaerocarpa*, *B. nuttalliana*, and *B. leucantha*). Although the parents and hybrids between any two species are easily identified

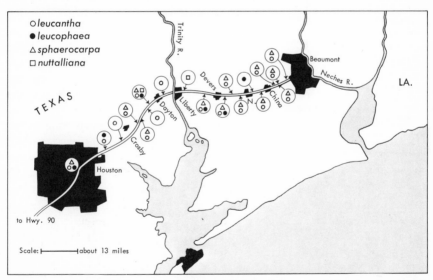

FIG. 10–4. Populations of *Baptisia* studied by Alston and Turner along U.S. Highway 90 between Houston and Beaumont, Texas. Each population contained hybrids that sometimes involved up to four species. Using exterior morphology they could detect no more than two species as involved in the hybrid swarms at any one locality. However, using species-specific flavonoids as identifying characters, up to four species were identified in certain populations. Symbols indicate the number of species involved in each population. (From Alston and Turner, 1968, by permission.)

on morphological grounds, backcrosses and hybrids involving three and four species are not. Alston and Turner (1963a) were, however, able to identify readily these more involved hybrid situations using the patterns of flavonoids, as can be seen in Figure 10–4.

Primary Gene Products (proteins)

Protein chemistry was, until recently, a rather undeveloped field of human inquiry, largely because of the technical difficulties involved in studying proteins. It had been known for a long time that proteins were formed by the repetition of very simple units called amino acids (Fig. 10–5). Molecules of this kind are called polymers. However, unlike starch and cellulose, which also are polymers (the repeating units in these molecules are sugars) in which only one or two repeating units are involved, the number of amino acids in protein polymers is over twenty. Also, unlike starch or cellulose, and this is of major importance, the twenty amino acids are not arranged in smaller repetitive units, but have a precise and unique sequence in each protein. A protein has anywhere from fifty to thousands of amino acid residues, with several hundred the most common number. The ways in which twenty amino acids can be arranged in groups of one hundred is astronomical:

$$C_{(100)}^{20} = \frac{100 \times (100 - 1) \times (100 - 2) \times \cdots (100 - 20 + 1)}{1 \times 2 \times 3 \times \cdots 20}.$$

It is this tremendous potential of variability that gives proteins the capacity to play the important role they have in the development of organisms.

However, not all theoretical arrangements of amino acids are possible for physicochemical reasons and also because many would probably not be biologically functional. Amino acids are characterized by the presence of carboxyl and amino groups attached to the same terminal carbon in the

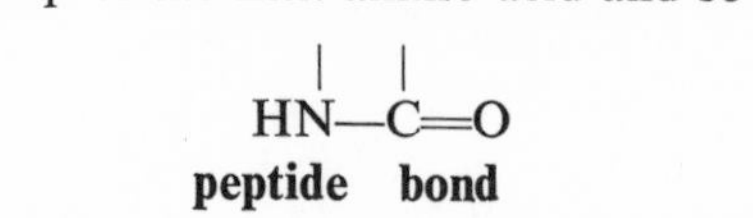

$$-C\!=\!O \qquad\qquad\qquad -NH_2$$
$$\searrow$$
$$OH$$

carboxyl   **amino**

molecule. The amino acids are linked to each other by means of a peptide bond, that is, a covalent bond between the amino group of one amino acid and the carboxyl group of the next amino acid and so on:

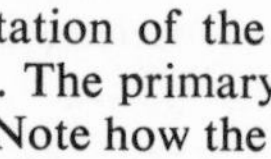

$$HN\!-\!C\!=\!O$$

peptide   bond

FIG. 10–5. Schematic representation of the primary, secondary, tertiary and quaternary structure of a protein. The primary structure is given by the order of the amino acids along the chain. Note how the chain may join through secondary bonds (in this case a disulfide bond) to other portions of the chain. Note also that a protein is a polymer formed of up to twenty amino acids. The secondary chain

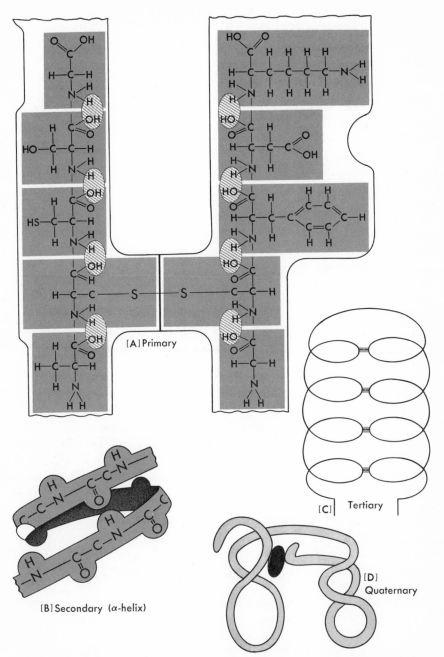

[A] Primary

[B] Secondary (α-helix)

[C] Tertiary

[D] Quaternary

is represented by a bending of the primary chain into an alpha helix; the tertiary structure is given by the bending of the secondary and primary chain so that secondary groups may react (as shown above). The quaternary structure is the final shape the molecule assumes; it may involve more than one polypeptide and also a prostetic group (indicated here by hatching).

In this way a backbone of peptide linkages is formed from which the residues of the various amino acids extrude. The order of the amino acids in the protein is known as the primary structure of the protein.

A protein will always have one end that is basic (the amino or **N** end) and one that is acidic (the carboxyl or **C** end). In addition, some amino acids (see Fig. 10–5) have reactive groups themselves, such as carboxyls, amino, or sulfidryl radicals, that can impart a charge to the molecule. It will be the tendency of any molecule, and proteins are no exception, to fold in such a way that charges of opposite sign will be neutralized. Proteins fold in different ways, known as the *secondary* and *tertiary structures*. The secondary structure refers to the various ways in which the molecule twists and spirals (particularly in what is called the *alpha helix*, by which every fifth amino acid comes into contact and is held in place by hydrogen bonding); tertiary structure refers to the various folds that the secondary-folded molecule engages in. The reaction of the side groups of the amino acid residues is in great part responsible for the tertiary structure of the protein. Whereas the secondary structure, the alpha helix, is a regular kind of folding with every fifth amino acid reacting with every other, the tertiary structure is not so. Amino acids quite far apart in the molecule are put into contact by the folding and allowed to react. Tertiary folding involves many kinds of chemical bonds, such as disulfide bonds, hydrogen bonds, ionic bonds, and hydrophobic bonds. The important thing to remember is that the effect of the secondary and tertiary folding of the protein is to reduce the net charge of the molecule and that as a result this folding imparts to the molecule a unique three-dimensional structure.

Some large proteins are made up of folded protein subunits called poly-peptides. In some, the molecule consists of only one chain; in others it contains two, four, or more. The aggregation of the subunits in these cases is termed *quaternary structure*. Quaternary structure is maintained by the same types of bonding as are involved in tertiary structure. Also, some proteins (called *conjugated proteins*) are formed by one or more polypeptide chains and a nonprotein component called a *prosthetic group*. Hemoglobin, the pigment in human red blood cells, is composed of four polypeptide chains (*globin*) and a nonprotein iron-containing prosthetic group (*heme*).

In what ways are proteins of use to the biosystematist? Their basic importance derives from the fact that they are characters that are determined by a single gene and consequently can serve as easily determined gene markers. This permits the population biologist to obtain estimates of genetic heterogeneity in a population and allows an assessment of the effect of the elements of the genetic system, the breeding system, and the environment on genetic heterogeneity in the population. We will look at some examples.

First, let us review the evidence on which the single gene inheritance of proteins is based. In a study of the enzyme leucine aminopeptidase (LAP) in corn, Beckman, Scandalios and Brewbaker (1964) crossed two lines that were each characterized by the possession of an enzyme with a different physical property. One line had a so-called *fast* enzyme; that is, when subjected to electrophoresis it moved faster toward the cathode than the so-called *slow* enzyme possessed by the other line. First and second filial generation crosses between the lines and backcrosses to the parental lines produced the results depicted in Table 10–1. It can be seen that the ratios obtained correspond to the expected ratios for the segregation of a pair of alleles. This experiment demonstrates that a pair of alleles controls the segregation of these two forms of the enzyme. It does not demonstrate, however, that there is necessarily only one pair of genes controlling the structure of the enzyme. It could be that the difference resides in the control of synthesis, in the attachment of some prosthetic group, or in the formation of another enzyme that interacts with LAP.

TABLE 10–1

Results of Crosses Made to Demonstrate the Genetic Control of the Leucine-Amino-Peptidase Enzyme Variants in Corn. The Genotypes Noted Within Brackets Are Deductions Fitting the Results. (From Beckman, Scandalios, and Brewbaker, 1964.)

		LAP Zones in the Offspring			
Female Parent	Male Parent	F [F/F]	F + S [F/S]	S [S/S]	Total
AA4(*F/F*)*	AA4(*F/F*)	30	0	0	30
P39(*S/S*)**	P39(*S/S*)	0	0	30	30
AA4(*F/F*)	P39(*S/S*)	0	30	0	30
P39(*S/S*)	AA4(*F/F*)	0	30	0	30
(AA4 × P39)(*F/S*)	AA4(*F/F*)	16	14	0	30
AA4(*F/F*)	(AA4 × P39)(*F/S*)	17	13	0	30
(AA4 × P39)(*F/S*)	P39(*S/S*)	0	10	20	30
P39(*S/S*)	(AA4 × P39)(*F/S*)	0	12	18	30
(AA4 × P39)(*F/S*)	(AA4 × P39)(*F/S*)	20	22	18	60

* AA4. Inbred line from the University of Hawaii.
** P39. Inbred line from Purdue University.

Proteins have been used very successfully in the determination of possible ancestors of allopolyploid species. Hall, Johnson, and collaborators in Sweden and the United States have been using the electrophoresis patterns of seed proteins to reconstruct the ancestors of hexaploid wheat with great success. Because in this case there is independent cytological and morphological evidence regarding these ancestors, this work is a check on the soundness of the method (Johnson and Hall, 1965).

Hunziker (1966) has applied the technique of analysis of seed proteins to establish relationships between isolated populations of a group of rare species of grasses, the *Agropyron scabriglume* complex found in Argentina (Fig. 10–6). In the first instance, two species were analyzed: the hexaploid *A. scabriglume* (21 II) and its presumed ancestor, the tetraploid *A. tilcarense* (14 II). Crosses between the two species yielded hybrids with varying degrees of fertility (Table 10–2). The fertility varied according to the geographic

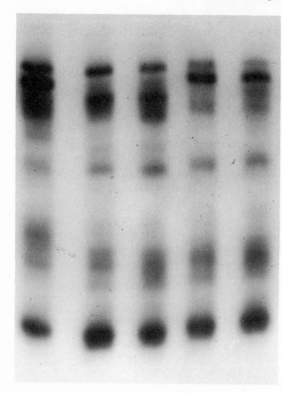

FIG. 10–6. Acrylamide gel patterns of seed proteins subjected to electrophoresis. From left, populations from (1) Tilcara, (2) El Carancho, (3) Balcarce, (4) Tafi, (5) San Martin. Note that gels 2 and 3, and gels 4 and 5, have identical patterns although they come from geographically different populations (see Fig. 10–7). For further details see text. (Photo, courtesy J. H. Hunziker.)

origin of the race of *A. scabriglume* employed in the cross. Highest fertility was obtained between a race of *A. scabriglume* from La Quiaca, Jujuy, in the mountains of northern Argentina, a locality less than one hundred miles from Tilcara (the sole known locality of *A. tilcarense*) and in approximately the same environmental and ecological conditions. These results led to an investigation through interspecific crosses and morphological and biochemical analysis of the various populations of *A. scabriglume* to determine the nature of the interspecific changes in this species. This study showed that the race of La Quiaca and that of Balcarce, a population from the plains of east-central Argentina and one thousand miles south of La Quiaca, differ by at least three reciprocal translocations, the hybrid between them being only 10% pollen fertile (Fig. 10–7). On the other hand, the race from Tupungato in west-central Argentina and that of Balcarce (separated also from each other by almost one thousand miles) are chromosomally almost identical. A fourth race, Carancho, from central Argentina and only three hundred miles west of Balcarce but several miles away from Tupungato (see Fig. 10–7) (Hunziker, 1967), also differs chromosomally from Balcarce by several translocations and inversions (Fig. 10–8). Analysis of the seed proteins, however, showed that Carancho and Balcarce (which are geographically and ecologically related) are virtually identical in their protein structure (and presumably in

TABLE 10-2

Chromosomal Associations and Seed Set in *Agropyron tilcarense, A. scabriglume* and Their Hybrids. (From J. Hunziker, 1966.)

Species or Hybrid and Geographical Origin	Chromosome Number	Chromosomal Associations. Mean Number in Metaphase I					Mean Number of Chiasma/Cell	Per Cent Fertile Seed
		I	II	III	IV	V–VI		
A. tilcarense (Tilcara)	28	0.07	13.96	0	0	0	33.1	93.5
A. scabriglume (La Quiaca)	42	1.04	20.48	0	0.02	0	—	86.9
A. scabriglume (Volcan)	42	0.29	20.79	0	0.03	0	37.9	83.8
A. scabriglume (Balcarce)	42	0.44	20.67	0	0.05	0	—	90.9
A. scabriglume (Tupungato × Balcarce)	42	0.36	20.50	0.03	0.14	0	—	95.1
A. scabriglume (La Quiaca × Balcarce)	42	3.76	14.15	1.38	1.29	0.12	—	10.4
A. tilcarense (Tilcara) × *A. scabriglume* (La Quiaca)	35	6.81	13.45	0.43	0	0	30.3	36.2
A. scabriglume (Volcan) × *A. tilcarense* (Tilcara)	35	4.94	10.44	1.78	0.73	0.18	30.1	11.2
A. tilcarense (Tilcara) × *A. scabriglume* (Tafi)	35	5.23	11.86	1.82	0.11	0.02	28.6	28.5
A. tilcarense (Tilcara) × *A. scabriglume* (Balcarce)	35	4.94	9.98	2.33	0.63	0.12	29.0	6.4
A. scabriglume (Balcarce) × *A. tilcarense* (Tilcara)	35	5.60	10.06	2.28	0.51	0.09	27.9	8.3
A. scabriglume (Tupungato) × *A. tilcarense* (Tilcara)	35	4.74	9.70	2.21	0.77	0.23	28.41	8.2

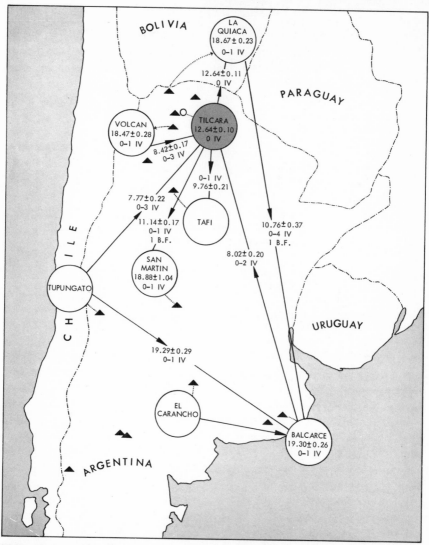

FIG. 10–7. Diagram indicating the geographical distribution of *Agropyron scabriglume* (triangles) and *A. tilcarense* (circles) and the crossing relationships among several of the populations. Figures indicate the value of closed bivalents and the standard error, and the number of quadrivalents (IV) and the maximum number of observed Bridge-fragments. (Modified from J. Hunziker, 1967, by permission.)

the genic makeup determining them), whereas Balcarce and La Quiaca are quite different (Fig. 10–6).

This example shows that in the *Agropyron scabriglume* complex, chromosomal rearrangements, and genic differentiation for seed protein, have not evolved at the same rate in all populations. It illustrates the complexity of

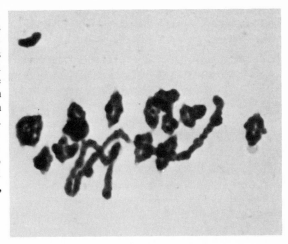

FIG. 10–8. Chromosomes at first metaphase of the cross between populations of *A. scabriglume* from El Carancho and Balcarce showing a chain of thirteen chromosomes, fourteen pairs and one univalent. In spite of this great chromosomal difference, the seed proteins of these two populations are almost identical (Fig.10–6).(Photo, courtesy J. Hunziker.)

evolution, and the necessity to study all aspects of the organism, such as morphology, anatomy, genetics, cytology, and chemistry, if the evolution of a species is to be really comprehended.

Protein Structure and Phylogeny

Another activity that is of direct interest to the systematist is the determination of the structure of homologous proteins in different organisms. Homologous proteins are those proteins that perform the same or similar function and that presumably have a common origin in some ancestral organism. In effect, if the kind and position of each amino acid in the primary structure of a homologous protein is known for several organisms, then it is possible to ascertain the minimum number of mutational steps that must have taken place to produce the difference. Once the primary structure of a homologous protein in two organisms is known, the differences can be interpreted in terms of mutations. The way this information is obtained is very simple. Because each amino acid is specified by one or more known triplets of DNA bases, all the possible triplets for the first conditions are stated, then those for the second; and the shortest path, that is, the one that requires the fewest mutational events, is chosen. For example, let us imagine that a protein X has the amino acid valine in position 3 in species I, alanine in species II, and glycine in species III. The codes for these amino acids are:

$$\text{Valine} \qquad \text{Alanine} \qquad \text{Serine}$$

$$\text{GUU} \overset{1}{\longleftrightarrow} \text{GCU} \overset{1}{\longleftrightarrow} \text{UCU}$$

$$\text{GUC} \overset{1}{\longleftrightarrow} \text{GCC} \overset{1}{\longleftrightarrow} \text{UCC}$$

$$\text{GUA} \overset{1}{\longleftrightarrow} \text{GCA} \overset{1}{\longleftrightarrow} \text{UCA}$$

$$\text{GUG} \overset{1}{\longleftrightarrow} \text{GCG} \overset{1}{\longleftrightarrow} \text{UCG}$$

We see that there are four possible paths, each requiring two single mutations, for the transformation of these amino acids. All other alternatives require more steps. Consequently, a mutational distance (called *patristic distance*) of 1 between each pair of organisms is established. The exact code cannot be hypothesized because there are four equally good ones. Let us now imagine that a fourth organism has arginine in position 3; the code for arginine is:

$$\text{Alanine} \qquad \text{Arginine} \qquad \text{Serine}$$

$$\text{GCA} \xleftrightarrow{2} \text{AGA} \xleftrightarrow{2} \text{UCA}$$

$$\text{GCG} \xleftrightarrow{2} \text{AGG} \xleftrightarrow{2} \text{UCG}$$

It takes a minimum of two steps now to change arginine into the amino acid present in species 1, 2, or 3 in position 3 in protein X. Also, only two of the four possible codes in species 1, 2, or 3 yield the change in two steps; the other two require three steps. Now a hypothetical phylogenetic tree can be constructed as follows:

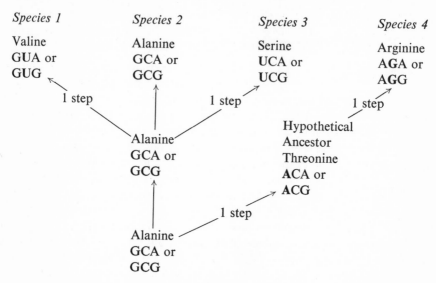

If we now count the steps separating the species along the branches, it can be seen that species 1 and 2 are separated by a distance of one, and 2 and 3 also by one; however, 1 and 3 are separated by a distance of two as are 2 and 4; 4 is separated from 1 and 3 by at least three steps.

If the position of every amino acid of a protein is known for many organisms, a phylogenetic tree can be constructed that reflects the possible relationships of descent, assuming that evolution has proceeded by the most direct path. So far, there has been very little of this kind of analysis because of the technical problems involved. In a study of the protein cytochrome c,

Fitch and Margoliash (1966) arrived at the phylogeny illustrated in Figure 10–9. Although the number of organisms sampled is still very small, the tree is in agreement with those proposed by zoologists and botanists in the past on more inductive methods, and it is also in agreement with data from the fossil record. In addition to furnishing independent evidence for previous findings, this method has the value of providing quantitative estimates of relationships. This method is a very promising one indeed.

This is just one way in which the findings of molecular biology will enrich the field of systematics. The future will no doubt see the development of a close collaboration between molecular biologists and systematists.

The study of proteins and enzymes for evolutionary and biosystematic purposes has barely begun. The techniques of electrophoretic separation and chromatographic analysis have, however, been developed now to the point where they can be applied relatively easily. This makes the analysis of large numbers of plants possible, and with it opens up the possibility of investigating by these means the genic composition of populations. In Chapter 7 some of the difficulties experienced by population geneticists in the past were mentioned, difficulties stemming largely from their inability to obtain accurate estimates of genic frequency. Protein and enzyme analysis promises to make possible the field of experimental population genetics.

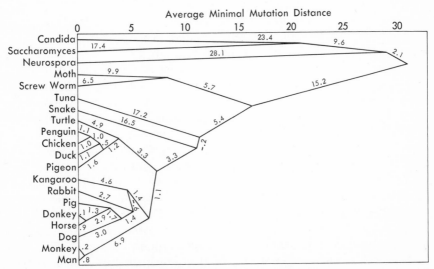

FIG. 10–9. Probable phylogeny for representative plants and animals computed through the study of the observable mutations in the cytochrome *c* gene, mutations that were inferred from the study of the amino acid sequence of the cytochrome *c* molecule in these organisms. Each number on the figure is the corrected mutation distance along the line of descent determined from the most parsimonious fit so far found, as explained in the text. (From Fitch and Margoliash, 1966, by permission.)

DNA Hybridization

One technique that is potentially very valuable for establishing relationships between organisms is that of DNA hybridization. This technique, as the name implies, consists of uniting two strands of DNA taken from two different species and measuring the degree to which they are complementary. Theoretically, two perfectly complementary strands should form a flawless double helix, and the degree to which they do not form the double helix should reflect the degree to which the two strands differ in their base-pair composition. In this manner it should be possible to obtain an exact estimate of the amount of difference in the genetic message carried by the two species being tested.

In practice, the technique consists of the extraction and purification of DNA from a species. This DNA is then labeled with a radioactive isotope (such as N^{15}) and then denatured (usually by gentle heating). When DNA is denatured, it unwinds, forming two simple strands. In one method the single strands of DNA are then placed in agar gel, which has the effect of minimizing contacts between the strands due to Brownian movement. In effect, when that happens the strands rewind, reforming the double helix which at this point in the procedure should be avoided. After this step, unlabeled, single-stranded DNA from another species (obtained in a similar manner) is then mixed with that of the first, and the two kinds of DNA are then allowed to react with each other, leading to the formation of double-stranded DNA. After that, the single-stranded DNA remaining is washed or filtered away. By measuring the relative amount of radioactive label in the two-stranded DNA formed by hybridization, the proportion of the DNA of the first species that hybridizes with that of the second can be estimated.

So far, DNA hybridization has been of limited value because of a series of unresolved technical problems that make the method relatively unreliable. However, some crude experiments (comparing a bacterium, a species of yeast, fish, mouse, and man, for example) have shown the potential of the method for estimating relationships. Some of the technical problems still remaining concern the existence of duplicated DNA within a single species (so-called redundant DNA), hybridization of DNA strands of the same species, and inability to estimate precisely the amount of DNA that has actually hybridized (present estimates are accurate only within a 2–5% error). The method remains, however, one of great potential (Britten and Kohne, 1968).

Areas for Further Study

Biochemical systematics is undoubtedly the most promising approach within biosystematics. The possibilities that it offers have just barely been explored.

Some of the promises of biochemical systematics are the following: (1) it permits a better definition of characters, both in terms of their inheritance and their ontogeny; (2) it permits a much more accurate estimate of relationships than has been possible so far, because the characters on which the estimate of relation are based can be better defined; (3) it permits more accurate estimates of gene flow, because minute phenotypic characteristics such as individual flavonoids or a particular enzyme can be measured. This area has been just barely investigated; and (4) it will permit the estimation of gene frequency in populations and of changes produced by various selective agents, as well as the effect on gene change of various elements of the genetic system. This will permit the development of the area of experimental population genetics.

Chapter 11

Mathematics and Statistics

No modern account of biosystematics can avoid discussing the role of mathematics and statistics. This would not have been the case fifty years ago; probably these subjects would not have figured in a textbook twenty-five years ago, either. In fact, it is only recently that a series of mathematical and statistical techniques has been developed to handle relationships between organisms. These techniques are often collectively lumped under the term *numerical taxonomy*. As we will see, numerical taxonomy is but one of many approaches. Consequently, a better collective term for these techniques is *statistical systematics* or *taximetrics*.

The impetus for the use of taximetrics and statistics was given by the modern high-speed digital computer (Fig. 11–1). In effect, taximetrics is based on the handling of large amounts of data, and computers are built to handle large amounts of data fast and efficiently. Before the availability of computers, the compilation of such simple statistics as a standard deviation for 10 characters in each of 50 samples consisting of 100 plants each (that is a total of 50,000 measurements) would take approximately three months of man-work; a computer resolves the problem in less than a minute at a cost of less than five dollars. And not only speed is gained, but accuracy; computers do not make mistakes, unless the machine breaks down, and when that happens it can easily be ascertained. Of the 500 man-computed standard deviations of our example, unless doublechecked at least 50 will be in error.[1] In addition, with the computer a series of computations can be undertaken that was not possible before, because of the time and effort it would have involved.

---

[1] The example given is that of the operations performed by the author in studying the *Gutierrezia sarothrae* complex (Solbrig, 1964) and discussed in Chapter 3.

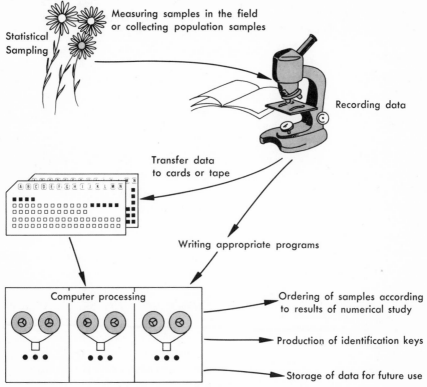

FIG. 11–1. Some of the operations performed during a taximetric study.

Statistics

In any given study, the time needed to assess all the plants of the kind under investigation always exceeds the time and effort that the investigator has available. The scientist, therefore, studies only some plants, which he hopes will be representative of the entire population. Statistics is the branch of mathematics that is concerned with the selection, description, and handling of samples and is consequently of direct concern to the scientist.

From the point of view of the biosystematist, statistics as a tool can be of major concern in three areas: (1) in the selection of representative samples; (2) in the description of the samples; and (3) in the analysis of interpopulational variation.

Sampling

Correct sampling is of utmost importance, and unless the sample is truly representative, all the data will be invalid. The cornerstone of correct sampling is that it has to be random. But as with many other concepts, there are problems in its practical application. From an absolute point of view, when it is said that a sample has to be random, this means that every plant has to have the same probability of being chosen as any other. An example is the case of the marsh aster, *Aster nemoralis*, a species found scattered in bogs and marshes of the eastern United States from Newfoundland to Delaware and west to Michigan. If a truly random sample of, for example, five thousand plants had to be chosen, a method would first have to be devised to give each plant the same chance of being chosen as any other, because that is the true meaning of a *random* sample. But how can this be done when there must be several thousand plants scattered over the northeastern United States and southern Canada? One possible method is first to choose in a random fashion a number of bogs where *Aster nemoralis* grows and then to choose a number of plants in each of these selected bogs. But because in some bogs the populations of *A. nemoralis* are larger than in others, a way has also to be devised to compensate for this. Otherwise, plants in small populations would have a higher probability of being chosen than those in large populations. And then, finally, a method has to be devised to pick bogs and plants within bogs at random. A possible method is to map carefully the bogs that contain *Aster nemoralis* and then number them consecutively from one on. A second step is to evaluate the number of plants growing in each bog and weigh each population accordingly. So, for example, a certain bog with one hundred plants is given twice as much representation as one with fifty plants by being numbered twice. Finally, either by dropping a series of papers in a container and then picking some out without deliberate choice or by the use of a table of random numbers, the scientist chooses five thousand plants that constitute a truly random sample. The exact number chosen depends on the investigator and the goal of the work. The larger the sample, the more representative it is, but also the more work is involved in obtaining the needed data.

It must be clear by now that this method is lengthy and time-consuming. Also, it is unlikely that all the populations of a species are known, and furthermore it is very improbable that the size of the populations is understood. In most cases it is impossible in taking a sample to give each plant exactly the same probability of being chosen as every other in the taxon under study. But it is possible to avoid making grossly biased estimates, be they conscious or not. For example, taking a fixed number of plants from a population rather than a fixed proportion introduces a small source of error, because plants in small populations will be overrepresented. However, unless the populations fluctuate greatly in their size or unless there is a direct effect of population size on the characteristics of the population, this error is not one that is going to produce a great difference in the outcome. Likewise, choosing for sampling those populations already known from herbarium specimens introduces a source of error, because it appreciably limits the statistical population. However, unless there is reason to believe that the populations represented in herbaria are different from those not yet represented in herbaria, the final results are not affected materially by this added error. By the same token, sampling by walking across a field and gathering the plant closest to the right foot every second step is not the ideal way, but is one that in most cases produces a reliable estimate. On the other hand, sampling only populations within twenty paces from a paved road and conspicuous enough for them to be spotted from a speeding car introduces a major source of error, because only a narrow ecological zone is being sampled, and only large populations within that zone. Also, if no provision is made as to how the sample will be gathered, and plants are collected presumably "at random" as the sampler walks through the population, it is likely that an error will be made, either consciously or not. In effect, it is probable in such an event that only plants within certain limits of variability will be sampled, because the sampler will have a mental image of the species and will tend unconsciously to collect the plants that most approximate it.

An important consideration when devising a sampling method is to ask oneself in every case if the added labor and time involved in refining a sampling procedure is going to improve considerably the accuracy of the data. So, for example, if the aim is to establish the limits of variability of a series of populations and to correlate them with latitude, the results will probably not be altered appreciably if only easily accessible populations along a highway are sampled. However, if montane and valley species are being compared, particularly if it is suspected that there may be some overlap in their variability, it is very important for a large number of populations in different ecological and altitudinal ranges to be sampled. In this, as in every other aspect of biology, common sense is a basic requirement, that is, the problem (the question to be answered) should determine the sampling method.

Statistical Descriptions of a Sample

The simplest application of statistics to systematics is the description of a single sample. Its purpose is to obtain reliable estimates of the true values of the characteristics of the population under study. The statistics of a single sample are relatively simple from the mathematical point of view. Nevertheless, they are fundamental from the point of view of the investigator. If the data with which he is dealing are not representative of the population, no other manipulation that he may perform will represent the population.

Statisticians have developed a series of rules and guidelines for the collection and analysis of samples to minimize all the possible errors that can be made. The biosystematist is, therefore, well advised to follow these rules. He should, however, remember that statistics is a tool in biosystematic investigation and not an end in itself. If the systematist follows blindly the guidelines set by the statistician, he may end up doing a great number of biologically meaningless exercises. Statistics is extremely useful, if not indispensable, but the biological questions to be answered should always be known in advance.

For a better understanding we will consider four aspects of the statistics of single samples. These are (1) choice of characters; (2) error and bias; (3) frequency distribution of characters; and (4) statistics of location and dispersion.

Choice of Characters

The choice of characters is a decision that has to be based by the biosystematist on biological and not statistical considerations. In preceding chapters the relative merits of various kinds of characters have been considered. For a description of the phenotype, morphological characters are most commonly employed. The reason for this is that the study of morphological characters requires the least manipulation and technical skill. However, genetic, cytological, and chemical characters can also be used to define the phenotype, as has already been discussed in previous chapters.

Characters must be quantifiable if they are to be employed for statistical analysis. Characters fall into two major categories. One kind, called *numerical characters* or *quantitative characters*, can be measured or counted, such as the length of a leaf, the number of petals in a corolla, or the diameter of a fruit. Numerical characters are of two kinds: those that show continuous variation, such as dimensions in general, where the character can have any value between two extremes, and those that show discontinuous variation, such as number of ovules in an ovary, teeth in a calyx, and so on, where the character can have only one of several states, but none in between. These latter are called *meristic characters*.

In contrast to numerical characters are the so-called qualitative or non-numerical characters. These are characteristics that cannot be measured, such as colors, complicated shapes, and so on. Nonnumerical characters can be coded numerically, however, and then treated as numerical characters. Colors can be coded following some standard chart on which each color is given a number. Shapes can also be coded. Other characters can be converted into measurable quantities by the use of suitable electronic equipment. The pattern of light absorption of a molecule or of a crude extract can be obtained and used as the character, or the distance from the origin of a protein band in an electrophoretic run can be measured and used as a character.

At this point we may ask what is a "character"? Is a leaf a character of the plant, or is the character the length, the width, the number of teeth in the margin of the leaf? Or perhaps the number of cells in the leaf or the amount of anthocyanin in these cells? Without entering into a philosophical discussion of the problem, suffice it to say that the investigator should remember what his intention is. If it is to describe the phenotype in as much detail as possible, he would be well advised to start with the cells and describe their properties, how they are integrated into tissues, and so on. However, the goal of the biosystematist is not to describe the phenotype in its totality, but to characterize it sufficiently so that the patterns of variation and the evolutionary relationships become clear. The question of what constitutes a "character" is therefore somewhat irrelevant to the problem at hand. What is important, however, is to be sure when establishing relationships that comparable characters are considered. Comparing the length of the leaf in one taxon with the shape of the leaf in another is not a valid comparison.

Measurement, Error, and Bias

In Table 11–1 are shown the results of a series of accurate measurements of a leaf performed by several investigators using the same measuring device. It can be seen that not all of these measurements agree. However, the leaf neither shrank nor expanded during that period. What the table indicates is that there is always a certain degree of error in every measurement that is performed. The nature and source of error in any study may be quite complex.

TABLE 11–1

Results of Ten Measurements Made on the Same Leaf with Exactly the Same Ruler by Ten Different Persons Working Independently and Unaware that a Comparison Was Being Made of Their Measurements.

Person	Measurements	Person	Measurements
1	5.0 mm	6	5.05 mm
2	4.9 mm	7	5.1 mm
3	4.95 mm	8	5.0 mm
4	5.0 mm	9	5.0 mm
5	5.0 mm	10	5.0 mm

Some of the sources of error are the following. First, the observer himself. He may have a tendency always to overestimate or underestimate or round off the observation to the nearest zero. He may be very meticulous, or he may be quite careless. All these personal variations will result in an observation that differs more or less from the true value. The error in the observer may also vary from time to time, depending on physical exhaustion, light conditions, and so on. Error also can depend on unconscious prejudice. It has been established that if the observer has a feeling about what the populational mean of a character should be, he will tend to round off to the lowest zero the highest values and to the highest zero the lowest values. An interesting and puzzling example is the original paper of Gregor Mendel on the basic principles of transmission genetics.

Sir Ronald Fisher (1936) has pointed out that Mendel probably had devised his genetic principles before he started his experiments and that he was producing a demonstration of his principles. Fisher bases this assertion on the fact that Mendel's ratios are consistently closer to expectation than sampling theory would lead one to expect. For yellow versus green seeds, for example, his F_2 numbers were 6,022 : 2,001, a deviation of 5 from the theoretical 3 : 1 ratio expected (6,017 : 2,006), whereas according to Fisher a deviation of 26 or more would be expected in half a large number of trials, each including 8,023 seeds. This by itself could be attributed to chance, but Mendel gets equally close approximations to expected ratios that are incorrect. In testing the F_2 dominants to see which of them are homozygous and which are heterozygous, Mendel took 10 seeds of the tested F_2 dominants and got a close agreement to the 1 : 2 ratio expected. However, as Fisher points out, in a test of only 10 seeds there is a 5% to 6% probability that a heterozygous plant will give all dominant offspring and therefore be classed as a homozygous. Consequently, the true expectation of Mendel's experiment was 1.8874 : 1.1126. Mendel's data are in very poor agreement with this expectation (Mendel's data should occur less than once in 2,000 trials), but in very close agreement with his incorrect expectation of 2 : 1.

This example is not intended to insinuate that Mendel doctored his data. On the contrary, Mendel's work exemplifies the experimental approach in biology at a time when such an approach was almost unheard of. What it indicates is the insidious nature of error in statistics. Mendel's data may have been unconsciously biased in a great many ways. Sturtevant (1965) insinuates three: (1) there may have been an unconscious tendency to classify somewhat doubtful individuals in such a way as to fit expectation; (2) there may have been some families that seemed aberrant and that were omitted as being probably wrong because of experimental error; and (3) some of the counts may have been made for him by assistants or students who were aware of his expectations and wanted to please him.

A second source of error is the measuring device. A balance that has not been accurately set to zero will always measure slightly more or less than the true value. A balance will also be affected by temperature and humidity, the extent depending on the type and quality. Equally, a ruler if poorly calibrated may over- or underestimate true length, or it may do one at one end and the other at the other end. A metal ruler will expand and contract with temperature changes, but not with humidity changes; a wooden ruler will do the opposite. Sensitive measuring devices are built so as to take these factors into consideration, and ambient changes can be minimized by taking measurements under standard conditions. However, although the error can be minimized, it can never be eliminated.

A final source of error is in the material itself. The sizes of any two leaves on a plant are different, so are any two flowers, cells, and so on. The size of the plant is different from day to day, as well as in the morning and in the evening, before watering and after. Some of this variation is biologically important and is worth discriminating (such as differences between populations); other variations are not.

The effect of all these sources of error is to decrease the reliability of the estimations that are made. For statistical purposes it is assumed that most errors balance each other out. However, this may not always be so, and the investigator should try to be aware of the many possible sources of error and try to keep them to a minimum.

Frequency Distribution of Characters

When an adequate sample is available it is often of interest to plot the frequency distribution of one or more characters. Such a graph permits the investigator to analyze the nature of the distribution.

The nature of the frequency distribution has biological and statistical implications, So, for example, a bimodal distribution (that is, one where there are two peaks, Fig. 11–2) may indicate that two different units are

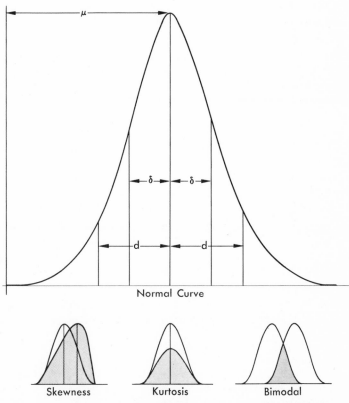

FIG. 11–2. In a normal distribution the mean μ fixes the position of the curve, and the standard deviation δ measures its spread. The bottom curves indicate deviations from normality likely to be encountered in biological samples: skewness, kurtosis, and bimodality.

being sampled or that the character in question is polymorphic. If the distribution is bimodal and unequal it may indicate a simple or complex genetic situation, or it may indicate a case of hybridization, and so on.

From the statistical point of view, a frequency distribution will point out if the distribution is a so-called normal distribution or not. The frequency distribution of the variation of the measurements of many biological characters and phenomena follows this particular "normal" distribution.[2] This does not mean that a distribution that is not "normal" necessarily reflects an error in measurement. So, for example, the distribution of genotypes in an F_2 generation resulting from the cross of a parent that is homozygous dominant for a set of independent genes with the corresponding homozygous recessive follows the formula $(\frac{1}{2} + \frac{1}{2})^k$, where k is the number of independent segregating genes. Only those characters that are the result of a multitude of factors acting more or less independently will tend to be "normally" distributed.

It is important to know if a character is normally distributed in order to apply further statistical manipulations correctly. In fact, most of the common statistical tests, such as the analysis of variance, were developed for normally distributed characters. It has been shown, however, that these tests still apply in cases of characters whose distribution deviates from normality. However, in such cases closer attention has to be paid to the tests of significance.

Statistics of Location and Dispersal

Once the data are gathered, there are several statistical parameters that can be obtained to aid in the objective comparison of the statistical populations under study.

The mean, mode, standard deviation (or variance), and coefficient of variability are the usual parameters that are calculated. They characterize the variability of a taxon very well with respect to the traits measured. The mathematical mean gives a figure that indicates the center of dispersion; the mode provides an indication of the most frequent classes. The values for the mode and the mean should be quite similar if the investigator is dealing with a normal curve of variability. If they are not, an explanation has to be found for the discrepancy before a normal distribution is assumed. Strong differences

---

[2] A "normal" curve can be defined as a symmetrical and continuous curve of which the shape shows a point of maximum slope on either side of the center line or axis of symmetry that corresponds to the mean, μ, the distance from this point of maximum slope to the center line corresponding to the standard deviation, δ.

The formula for the normal curve is

$$m = \frac{1}{\delta\sqrt{2\pi}}\, e^{-\frac{(x-\mu)^2}{2\delta^2}}$$

where m is the frequency of the character x, δ the standard deviation, and μ the mean of the sample.

between the modal and mean values can, for example, indicate a simple genetic ratio, such as the one produced by a pair of genes.

A case in point is exemplified by *Dithryea wislizenii*, a small herb in the family Cruciferae that grows in western Oklahoma and Texas and west into southern Utah, Nevada, Arizona, New Mexico, and northwestern Mexico. It is commonly found in sandy and loose granitic soils and often forms large populations of several thousand individuals. The fruits are normally pubescent, but occasionally glabrous fruits are found. The character glabrous fruit was the basis for the description of a new species, *Dithryea griffithsii*, by the American botanist Standley. Rollins (1958) observed one population in which plants with glabrous and pubescent fruits were found growing together. A rough field estimate showed that plants with pubescent fruits were about three times as common as plants with glabrous fruits. All observed plants possessed either glabrous fruits or pubescent fruits, and none showed a graduation from one condition to the other. Open-pollinated offspring from two glabrous- and two pubescent-fruited plants showed that, whereas the glabrous plants segregated for this character, the pubescent fruits bred true. Controlled crosses (Table 11–2) confirmed this and furthermore showed that the character could be interpreted as due to one single pair of segregating genes, *G* and *g*, the glabrous condition being the dominant one.

This last is a paradox. The field observations indicated that pubescent is the common character, being roughly three times as common as glabrous. However, it is the recessive character. If it were selectively neutral and both alleles were equally frequent in the population, pubescent fruits should be less prevalent. If, on the other hand, selection favors pubescent over glabrous, the dominant *G* gene should be much less frequent or nonexistent. This then is another case of polymorphism, and it is likely that the heterozygous is being favored, although it still remains to be proved.

The statistical parameter, range, is poor as an estimate of variability for three main reasons. First, it is highly dependent upon the sample size. The larger the sample, the higher the probability that the sample range will also be larger. Secondly, there is no way of estimating the true range of variability

TABLE 11–2

Results of Crosses Between Glabrous and Pubescent Plants of *Dithryea wislizenii*. (Data from Rollins, 1958.)

		Progeny			
		Pubescent		Glabrous	
Parents	N	Obtained	Expected	Obtained	Expected
Glabrous × glabrous	70	18	17.5	52	52.5
Glabrous × pubescent	76	48	38	28	38
Pubescent × pubescent	118	118	118	0	0

of the population from the sample range, and it is this last estimate that is wanted. Finally, the sample range does not give an idea of the relative distribution of the various classes. The reason that, in spite of its limited statistical value, the range is almost universally presented in taxonomic works is twofold: first, its ease of observation and of calculation, only the smallest and largest specimens need to be measured; second and most important, the taxonomist is very interested in finding distribution gaps in order to construct dichotomous keys. For this purpose calculating the range is the best strategy.

A much better measure of dispersion is the variance or the standard deviation (the square root of the variance). The variance is the sum of the squares of the deviations $(\overline{X} - X)^2$ from the mean divided by the sample size minus one $(N - 1)$

$$s^2 = \frac{(X - X)^2}{N - 1}$$

The reason that the variance is such a good measure of dispersion will not be immediately obvious. Its justification is to be found in probability theory and the theory of the testing of hypotheses. In any case, variance does give the best estimate of dispersion available and should be calculated whenever populational studies are undertaken. Because the variance is often a large number, the standard deviation, that is, the square root of the variance, is given instead.

The standard deviation and the variance cannot be used for comparative purposes, because their value is dependent on that of the mean. It stands to reason that the variations around the mean for plant size of a *Sequoia* tree will be much larger than those around a pansy. To compare the relative variability of a population of redwoods and of pansies, another measure of variability has to be calculated, the coefficient of variability

$$V = \frac{100s}{\overline{x}}$$

The coefficient of variability is the standard deviation divided by the mean and multiplied by 100 in order to get a higher number. The value for animal populations is usually 5%, according to Simpson, Roe, and Lewontin (1960). Lower values indicate incomplete sampling, higher ones probably mixed populations. The values for plant populations are much higher, around 10% to 20%, reflecting the higher variability and flexibility of plants.

When an investigator is dealing with large samples and several characters, the mechanics of obtaining the mean, mode, standard deviation, and coefficient of variability are very tedious and time-consuming. The investigator should seriously consider in such situations the feasibility of availing himself of the services of an electronic computer. Several standard programs are available for obtaining these parameters.[3]

[3] Modern desk calculators with limited memories and print-out devices will also aid in speeding up the calculations.

With the mean, mode, standard deviation, and coefficient of variability, the variation of a population is well characterized. In order to compare the characters of different populations and evaluate the statistical significance of differences between populations, as well as to make predictions about the real values of the populations rather than the samples, a number of tests have been devised. These can be found together with their rationale in any statistical text.

Interpopulation Variation and Significance Tests

The biosystematist when turning to statistics will be mostly interested in testing the validity of certain assumptions about his samples. The samples will come in most likelihood from different geographical localities and may represent different evolutionary units. Once the sample has been described adequately in a statistical form, the distribution plotted, and the mean, variance, and other appropriate statistics calculated, it is likely that most samples will differ in many or all the statistics. The biosystematist will probably have enough understanding of his plants by then to make a working hypothesis to explain this variation. Hypotheses in such a situation will fall into two broad categories to the effect that (1) the differences in the sample represent real, biologically meaningful differences in the natural population sampled; or (2) the differences in the sample do not represent a biologically meaningful difference in the population. Statisticians have developed a series of statistical procedures, or tests, to gauge the probability that the difference in the sample represents a real difference in the natural populations.

These tests, usually known as *tests of significance*, should not be applied blindly, however. It must be remembered that any two populations differ, if ever so slightly, in the frequency of their genes. Consequently, if refined statistics are applied, this difference will be bared. It is, therefore, not enough to ascertain if a difference exists between populations, but also the magnitude of the difference. Another necessary step is to find a reasonable explanation for the probable cause of the difference. So, for example, a difference of 5 mm in the diameter of the capitulum of two populations of sunflowers may be statistically significant, that is, it represents a true difference between the populations. But does it represent a biologically meaningful and significant difference? Hardly. Such a small difference is to be expected between any two populations. Only the application of other criteria, such as those discussed in this book, can evaluate meaningfully the significance of populational differences in the phenotype.

Taximetrics

In comparing two or more samples, the investigator may wish to have a criterion for evaluating their overall similarity. One such measure is the hierarchical taxonomic system. If two populations, A and B, are considered to belong to the same subspecies of a species, whereas a third population, C, is placed in a different species of the same genus, and a fourth population, D, is placed in a different genus, the implication is that A and B are more similar to each other than to C and D, and that A, B, and C are more similar to each other than any is to D.

However, when more than two populations are in the same category, it is impossible to ascertain on the basis of their taxonomic rank their overall similarities. Furthermore, the classical way by which populations are arranged in a taxonomic hierarchy usually does not assign numerical values to the overall similarities. Taximetrics, or numerical taxonomy, is an attempt to assign numerical values to the degree of similarity between taxonomic units and to construct a classification on the basis of these numerical similarity values. According to Sokal and Sneath (1963), numerical taxonomy can be defined as "the numerical evaluation of the affinity or similarity between taxonomic units and the ordering of these units into taxa on the basis of their affinities."

Numerical taxonomy has been the center of heated controversy in the last ten years, and its practitioners have often been pitted against the rest of the taxonomic community. This is very unfortunate, particularly because the controversy has centered around the merits or demerits of the concept rather than the method, where the real problem lies.

The attempt to assign numerical values to the similarity between organisms is not a new matter. The French botanist and naturalist, Adanson, in the eighteenth century was the first to work out such a scheme. No useful method had been developed until recently, however. One of the reasons is that any meaningful index will, of necessity, involve a large number of calculations. Before the advent of the electronic computer, the computational difficulties were such that it was not practical to use these indices.

Numerical values representing the degree of overall similarity of two or more organisms will greatly aid not only the taxonomist interested in producing a classification, but also the biosystematist who is trying to understand the reasons for the differences and similarities between taxa. The problem lies in obtaining an index that is valid and of universal application. So far, none of the proposed indices has met with universal approval, there being some objections to each one of them.

Basically, three major kinds of indices have been proposed: (1) coefficients of association; (2) coefficients of correlation; and (3) coefficients of distance.

Coefficients of Association

To obtain a coefficient of association between two taxonomic units, all the characters of both units are first given one of two possible scores: + or − (or 1 or 0). They are then arranged in a 2 × 2 matrix in the following manner:

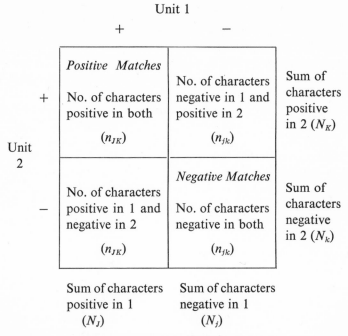

The fundamental formula for all the different coefficients of association proposed consists of the number of matches divided by a term implying the possible number of comparisons:

$$\text{Coefficient of association} = \frac{\text{Number of matched characters}}{\text{Possible number of comparisons}}$$

The problems in arriving at a universally acceptable coefficient of association are the following. (1) Should the numerator include only those characters that are positively matched, that is, when the character is present in both species, or should it also include those that are negatively matched, that is, when the character is absent in both species? (2) Should both matched and unmatched characters be equally weighted, or should either matched or unmatched characters be more heavily weighted when deciding on a value for the denominator?

A drawback of the coefficients of association is that all characters have to be given only one of two states. These coefficients are therefore best suited for studies in which most of the characters are of that nature, such as presence or absence, and least for studies in which most characters are continuous in their distribution, such as measurements in general (Fig. 11–3).

Coefficients of Correlation

In obtaining this kind of coefficient the characters do not have to be scored in a + or − way, but their true values can be used. The coefficient is obtained

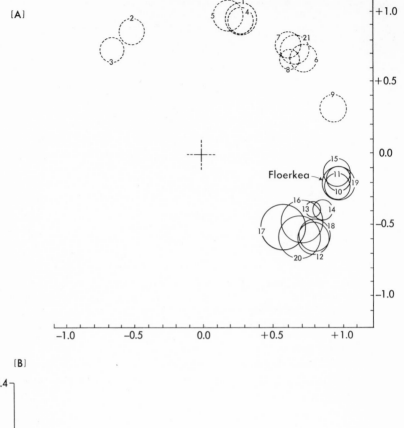

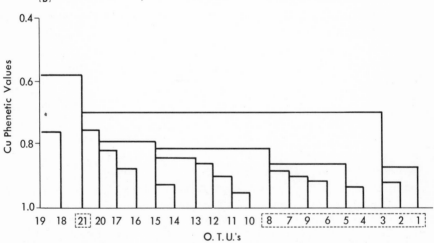

FIG. 11–3. Two ways of representing the results of taximetric studies using indices of similarity. A. Cluster analysis of twenty-one taxa of Limnanthaceae using only vegetative characters; B. Same taxa with the relationships depicted using a phenogram and using all characters. In the vegetative analysis, similarity is indicated by physical closeness of the circles each of which represents an OTU; (Operational Taxonomic Unit) in the phenogram similarity is read along the ordinate where horizontal lines connect two taxa (indicated by numbers on the ordinate). (From Ornduff and Crovello, 1968.)

by calculating the product-moment correlation in the following way (Sokal and Sneath, 1963):

$$rjk = \frac{\sum\limits_{i=s}^{n} (Xij - \bar{X}j)(Xik - \bar{X}k)}{\sum\limits_{i=1}^{n} \sqrt{(Xij - \bar{X}j)^2(Xik - \bar{X}k)^2}}$$

where j and k stand for the two units (species, populations, and so on) being compared, and X_{ij} stands for the value of character i in unit j, and X_{ik} stands for the value of character i in unit k. $\bar{X}_j$ and $\bar{X}_k$ stand for the mean for all characters in units j and k respectively; n is the number of characters.

This coefficient is best suited to characters that are measurements. When coded characters are introduced, a problem arises, because this might lead to spurious correlations. A problem also arises when the number of states varies from character to character, as when one character is scored on an absence or presence basis and another, such as flower color, on a 1 to 10 scale. This last problem can, however, be dealt with by statistical manipulation, though at the cost of increased computer time.

Coefficients of Distance

Measures of distance are based on a geometrical model. A species is supposed to occupy a point in a multidimensional space (the number of dimensions being equal to the number of characters). The distance coefficient between any two taxa is an index of the distance between the points in this multidimensional space (Fig. 11–4).

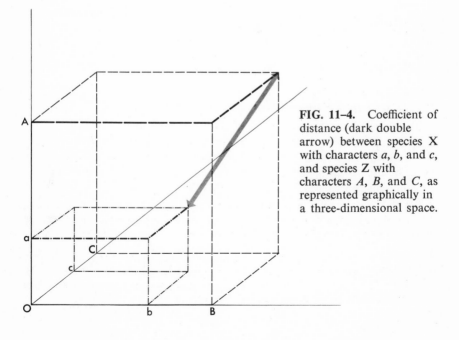

FIG. 11–4. Coefficient of distance (dark double arrow) between species X with characters a, b, and c, and species Z with characters A, B, and C, as represented graphically in a three-dimensional space.

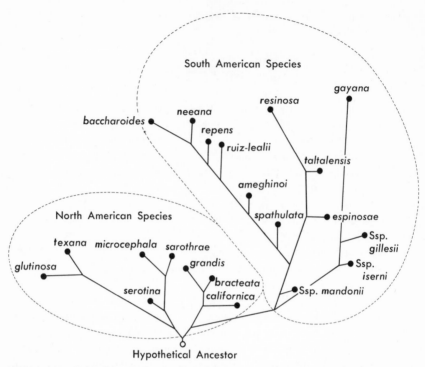

FIG. 11–5. Probable phylogeny for the genus *Gutierrezia* produced by a computer using a total of twenty-one characters and using a program developed by J. Farris of the State University of New York and which uses a modified distance coefficient. The lines separating any two species are a measure of the most probable evolutionary path. Note how the computer separated the North and South American species into two independent evolutionary lines, and also how it considers the North American species to be more primitive. This corresponds with evidence obtained independently.

With this method there are several computational drawbacks, particularly if new characters are added after a computation is made. In effect, in such a case a new dimension is added to the space and each species acquires a new location. There is also the problem that the distance increases with the number of characters, so that some kind of average distance has to be calculated. Nevertheless, distance coefficients have been used, particularly the so-called Mahalanobis generalized distance (Fig. 11–5).

Any numerical index estimates relations in a precise and repeatable way. It is therefore a great step over subjective criteria. However, the fundamental question is not its repeatability, but its biological meaning. At present, whenever possible, it is recommendable to apply more than one type of index and see if the different indices produce results that are appreciably different.

For the biosystematist, numerical taxonomic methods offer a procedure that allows him to evaluate objectively phenotypical similarities between populations. When combined with genetic, cytological, ecological, and chemical studies, these methods promise a realistic estimation of the course of evolution.

Simulation Studies

Last, but not least, another approach made possible by the electronic computer should be mentioned. That is the ability to produce simulation models.

By simulation is meant the programming of a digital computer to behave as the biosystematist suspects the population does. By assigning numerical values to a series of variables, such as mutation, gene flow, selection, and fitness, to name just a few, he can observe the interaction between these forces over a number of generations.

Simulation models can be deterministic, or they can be stochastic. In deterministic models each event has one possible outcome. In a stochastic model each event can have more than one outcome, each outcome having a certain probability. Using devices such as choosing random numbers, the computer decides which outcome for a given event will take place. A stochastic model is probably closer to nature and is to be preferred over a deterministic one.

Simulation permits preliminary testing of hypotheses. If the simulation model indicates that an event will not occur, there is probably no use in testing it with live plants. Rather, a modification of the hypothesis is called for. On the other hand, positive results only confirm that the hypothesis is plausible. Experiments with true organisms should be set up in order to prove the theory. The model, by necessity, contains only some of the variables present in nature, and it is always possible that the unknown ones are in some way controlling the evolutionary event being tested. Only experiments with live plants can determine this.

Chapter 12

Conclusion

Systematic studies are basically comparative studies. Breeding populations, individual plants, and organs, tissues, and so on, from different organisms are studied, emphasizing their similarities and differences. However, systematic studies are primarily concerned with comparisons of species rather than individuals or parts of individuals. This requires, however, that it be known first what constitutes a species. We have seen in previous chapters that this is not always easily ascertained. The first task of the biosystematist is to circumscribe and define individual species in order to make more detailed comparative studies possible. Comparative studies also offer a unique opportunity to synthesize diverse kinds of knowledge about the individual plant accumulated by the more analytically minded biologists and to interpret this knowledge in terms of selection and evolution. This is not an easy task, either, because the various branches of biology have become very specialized and the data that have been collected, the theories that have been proposed, and the experiments that have been performed are legion, and the information is scattered through scores of specialized journals.

The third major task that the biosystematist has to perform is to explain the origin and evolution of the species he is studying. This requires an understanding of the biology of populations, and particularly of genetic phenomena. Basically, then, the role of the biosystematist is to interpret the diversity of organisms in the framework of modern biology.

The smaller the particle studied, the more general and universal the findings usually are. The second law of thermodynamics is truly universal. Most of the findings of the physicochemist and the molecular biologist apply to all biological systems. So, for example, there is not much variation in the shape, chemical composition, and function of mitochondria and their universal occurrence in cells. Meristematic tissues, however, are not universally the same, and whole organs, such as flowers and leaves, show a much greater amount of diversity from species to species and can even be totally absent. The systematist is interested in diversity, and it is not surprising that he has obtained most of his information from the great diversity shown by plant organs and tissue systems. A truly synthetic approach requires, however, that all aspects of the plant be considered. The emphasis on diversity through the study of the morphology and anatomy of organs also often leads to a de-emphasis in systematic studies on those evolutionary processes of universal occurrence and to a preoccupation with characteristics of the plant that are biologically unimportant. It is the role of the biosystematist to emphasize

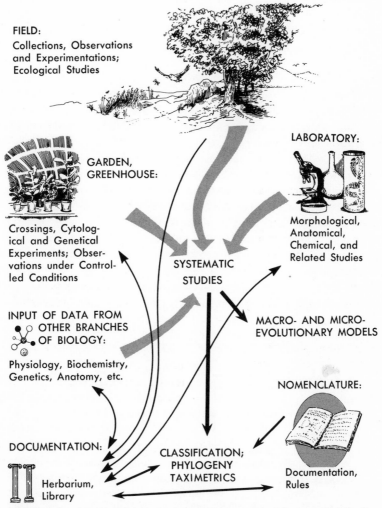

FIELD:
Collections, Observations and Experimentations; Ecological Studies

LABORATORY:

GARDEN, GREENHOUSE:

Crossings, Cytolog-ical and Genetical Experiments; Obser-vations under Control-led Conditions

Morphological, Anatomical, Chemical, and Related Studies

SYSTEMATIC STUDIES

INPUT OF DATA FROM OTHER BRANCHES OF BIOLOGY:

Physiology, Biochemistry, Genetics, Anatomy, etc.

MACRO- AND MICRO-EVOLUTIONARY MODELS

NOMENCLATURE:

DOCUMENTATION:

Herbarium, Library

CLASSIFICATION; PHYLOGENY TAXIMETRICS

Documentation, Rules

FIG. 12–1. Some of the operations performed in Biosystematic Studies. (From Solbrig, 1966.)

diversity and similarity equally and to try to ascertain the biological meaning of the characteristics of the plant.

In this book some of the salient problems that the biosystematist has to solve and some of the techniques of study have been presented. In Chapter 2 the basic principles of the Theory of Evolution were explained. Darwinism constitutes the basic theoretical framework of biosystematics. Chapter 3 explored some of the salient aspects of variability in plants. Variability is the Gordian knot of taxonomy and systematics. If it is understood why and in what ways populations vary from other populations in the same and other species, the major difficulty in the way of an understanding of the species has been resolved. In Chapter 4 the breeding system was explored. The kind of breeding system of a plant will determine its pattern of morphological and genetic variability and sets limits to its evolutionary potential. Chapters 5, 6, and 7 explored problems associated with the evolution and circumscription of the species. This is the area that preoccupies most of the attention of the biosystematist. It was shown that the problem is intricate because species are not objects that are definable in the same way that inanimate objects are. Instead, they are states of a continuum in time, of a tree or web where species are constantly changing, splitting in two, or joining with others through hybridization or becoming extinct. Consequently, it is impossible to find a "norm" or "typical species." Rather than try to neatly pigeonhole all plants into rigid niches called species, the biosystematist ought to try to understand why the more complex situation exists. It is here that the challenge lies.

The last four chapters of the book briefly analyzed some of the approaches used by the biosystematist in his quest for understanding (Fig. 12–1). However, a very important aspect was omitted, namely, comparative morphology and comparative anatomy.

Comparative morphology is the basic approach of the systematist. The exterior morphology of the plant is the most accessible and consequently the easiest to study. The internal anatomy is not quite as accessible, and it

TABLE 12–1

References on Morphology and Anatomy Suggested for Further Reading.

BOLD, H. C. 1957. *Morphology of Plants*. New York, Harper & Brothers.

CARLQUIST, S. J. 1961. *Comparative Plant Anatomy*. New York: Holt, Rinehart & Winston.

EAMES, A. J. 1961. *Morphology of the Angiosperms*. New York: McGraw-Hill.

―――― AND L. H. MacDANIELS. 1947. *An Introduction to Plant Anatomy*. New York: McGraw-Hill.

ESAU, K. 1960. *Anatomy of Seed Plants*. New York: John Wiley & Sons.

―――― 1953. *Plant Anatomy*. New York: John Wiley & Sons.

FOSTER, A. S. AND E. M. GIFFORD, JR. 1959. *Comparative Morphology of Vascular Plants*. San Francisco: W. H. Freeman & Co.

SALISBURY, F. B. AND R. V. PARKE. 1964. *Vascular Plants: Form and Function*. Belmont, Calif.: Wadsworth Publishing Co.

requires specialized knowledge to fix and prepare tissues for study as well as to interpret them. Both morphology and anatomy are necessary in order to describe the plant. Only when the characteristics of the plant are known can the biosystematist try to interpret their evolution. Because this is such a basic operation that is adequately covered in most general textbooks, no further emphasis will be laid on it here. For the reader who may not be familiar with morphology and anatomy, some special references are given in Table 12–1. Two other points should be briefly mentioned before closing this presentation. One is the question of methodology, the other that of presentation of results.

Modern Methodology

The successes of modern biology are intimately connected to the development of a series of new techniques and apparatus, particularly in biochemistry: X-ray diffraction; nuclear resonance spectrography; infrared, visible, and ultraviolet spectrography; gel and paper electrophoresis; the different kinds of chromatography; amino-acid analyzers; the use of radioactive isotopes, to name just the most important techniques, today permit the separation of individual compounds from mixtures and their structural analysis. None of these techniques was available twenty-five years ago. Awareness of the possibility of new and better ways and a will to develop these ways has produced these apparatus and techniques.

Systematists are now using these approaches to advantage. They are also starting to use to advantage the electronic computer, which promises to become the most important tool in systematic research. What are needed now are devices for the automatic, fast, and accurate measurement of plant characters. Only when the hundreds of data that are needed for a statistical analysis of variation can be gathered relatively quickly and effortlessly will it be possible to use the electronic computer to full advantage. These faster devices are needed for recording morphological, cytological, and chemical characters.

Biosystematics to be truly synthetic has to amass data from various fields: molecular, developmental, and evolutionary biology and ecology. This is very time-consuming. Any effort to speed up and automatize the procedure without loss of accuracy will be a great boon to the field.

Presentation of Results

Results of systematic studies are published usually in the form of monographs, synopses, or floras. Theoretical discussions are usually published separately in the form of discussion papers.

The basic treatise in systematics is the monograph. In a monograph all the species of a genus, or less frequently of a family, are described and named. Ideally, the description is succinct, almost telegraphic, and deals largely or exclusively with external morphology. Although variation is indicated, it is confined to indications of the statistical range, and generally no data on populations are given. By and large vegetative characters are treated less carefully than floral ones. Appended to the description, more or less complete lists of specimens studied are given. In addition, keys are provided that allow the identification of unnamed specimens by the reader.

A synopsis is a less detailed treatise than a monograph, and a flora treats all the taxa of a given geographical region in synopsis. Both kinds of work

ELEMENTARY KEY TO SOME MICHIGAN OAKS IN WINTER

```
   1A.  END BUDS OVER 3/16 INCH
     2A.  END BUDS BROAD OR BLUNT
       3A.  TWIGS HAIRY
                   . . . . . . . . . .  QUERCUS MACROCARPA
       3B.  TWIGS HAIRLESS OR NEARLY SO
                   . . . . . . . . . .  QUERCUS COCCINEA
     2B.  END BUDS NARROW, SHARP
       4A.  END BUDS HAIRLESS
         5A.  BARK LIGHT
                   . . . . . . . . . .  QUERCUS MUEHLENBERGII
         5B.  BARK DARK
                   . . . . . . . . . .  QUERCUS RUBRA
       4B.  END BUDS HAIRY
                   . . . . . . . . . .  QUERCUS VELUTINA
   1B.  END BUDS UNDER 3/16 INCH
     6A.  END BUDS BROAD OR BLUNT
       7A.  SHRUB
                   . . . . . . . . . .  QUERCUS PRINOIDES
       7B.  TREE
         8A.  ACORN SHORT-STALKED
                   . . . . . . . . . .  QUERCUS ALBA
         8B.  ACORN LONG-STALKED
                   . . . . . . . . . .  QUERCUS BICOLOR
     6B.  END BUDS NARROW, SHARP
       9A.  END BUDS HAIRLESS
         10A.  STUBBY PIN-LIKE BRANCHES ABSENT
                   . . . . . . . . . .  QUERCUS ELLIPSOIDALIS
         10B.  STUBBY PIN-LIKE BRANCHES NUMEROUS
                   . . . . . . . . . .  QUERCUS PALUSTRIS
       9B.  END BUDS HAIRY
                   . . . . . . . . . .  QUERCUS IMBRICARIA
```

FIG. 12–2. Computer-constructed key to the Michigan oaks in winter. This key was produced by a computer programmed by Larry E. Morse of Michigan State University. Using a matrix of characters and taxa, the program finds the most useful character for each dichotomy, repeating the process until all taxa have been separated. Then the key is printed according to the programmed format (in this case in an indented format). In this example, the twig and bud characters are weighted more heavily than the other characters, and thus are used whenever possible. (Courtesy Larry E. Morse, reproduced by permission.)

follow, although in less detail, the formal pattern of a monograph with its emphasis on external morphology.

The monograph, the synopsis, and the flora have served their purpose very well. They permit the retrieval of information in a very efficient way, and they occupy the least possible amount of space on account of the concise style in which they are written.

However, new technology is available that promises to improve this. Factual information can now be stored in computers and retrieved automatically. Computers can be programmed to write identification keys at command, to distinguish between any two or more species that the user would like to discriminate. So, for example, if the investigator knows that he has a plant of *Quercus* from Michigan the computer can print a key for the identification of the species of *Quercus* from Michigan rather than for the whole United States (Fig. 12–2). It is very likely that some time in the near future descriptions and factual data will be stored on magnetic tape rather than in books, in formats no different from present-day monographs, from which they will be retrieved and printed as the need arises.

In the meantime, there is a need to include in monographs more information on aspects other than the external morphology of individual specimens. Many monographs (and some floras) today include data on cytology, genetics, and anatomy. However, these data are often included as appendices to the works; the main emphasis still seems to be on the classification and description of the external morphology for purposes of identification rather than of synthesis.

There is a need to change the format of the monograph to permit a greater emphasis on populational phenomena. Without neglecting the identifying and descriptive aspects of systematics, a better balance with the functional and dynamic aspects of populational phenomena must be achieved. Finally, an explicit effort should be made to state how good a fit the data present with theoretical prediction.

Some Problems and Challenges

The scientific and rigorous study of the diversity of living organisms has barely begun. Aside from the great magnitude of the task itself, there are several challenging problems that biosystematics offers.

A very important area that needs to be investigated is the genetic structure of populations. How diverse genetically are populations? To what extent does the breeding system affect the genetic structure of the population? How much heterozygosity is there in the population? Until recently there was no practical way to estimate gene frequencies in populations. The new method of gel electrophoresis of proteins and enzymes reviewed in Chapter 10 permits the biosystematist to obtain estimates for certain genes in the population in a more or less efficient way. Furthermore, the electronic computer allows the elaboration of complex mathematical models. A combination of the two techniques should yield important data on the genetic structure of the population.

Another challenging area has to do with levels of organization. Given that natural selection acts on phenotypes, how are cellular characteristics selected? Given that there are physicochemical restraints imposed on chemical reactions in the cell, how do they in turn restrain evolution? For example, the number of theoretically possible proteins is astronomical (page 166). However, only a very limited number of these proteins is found in living organisms. Why is this so? Is there some special property associated with those proteins that exist in living organisms, or is it a matter of chance?

Another interesting question relates to the diversity of living organisms themselves. Why are some plants annuals and others perennials? Why are some inbreeders, others outbreeders, and still others apomictic? What forces mold the evolution of these plants and how?

The study of the diversity of living organisms presents a great challenge. And it is not only an intellectually fascinating challenge, but a very practical one, too. Man has so far paid too little attention to his environment and the way he has been modifying it. Polluted air, polluted water, and sterile soil over ever increasing surfaces of the earth are clear signs that such a situation cannot continue. To proceed intelligently, we must first know what forces have shaped the environment we call natural. Here is where the knowledge of the biosystematist is needed.

Glossary

Achaene. A dry, dehiscent, one-seeded fruit, characteristically found in the sunflower family (Compositae).

acuminate. Said of an acute apex whose sides are somewhat concave and taper to a protracted point.

agar gel. A gelatinous substance extracted from an alga and extensively used as a base for culturing microorganisms.

alleles. One of a pair or series of forms of a gene that are alternative in inheritance because they are situated at the same locus in homologous chromosomes.

allopatric. Said of taxa whose geographical ranges do not overlap.

allopolyploidy. A type of polyploidy characterized by containing genetically different sets of chromosomes from different species.

alpha helix. A regular configuration into which the primary chain of a polypeptide often folds. The helix is held together by hydrogen bonds between the carbonyl group of one residue and the amino group of the fourth residue down the chain.

amino group. $-NH_2$, a chemical group characteristically basic because of the addition of a proton to form ammonium ($-NH_3^+$).

analysis of variance. In statistics, a set of procedures for determining the degree of difference in the variability of two or more samples.

anatomy (plant). The study of the internal structure of a plant.

aneuploidy. The existence of more (or less) than the basic chromosome number in a normal plant, which is not an exact multiple of the basic number.

anther. The pollen-bearing part of the stamen borne at the top of the filament, or sometimes sessile.

anthocyanin. A water-soluble pigment, characteristic of red- and blue-colored flowers.

apomixis. Reproduction in which sexual organs or related structures take part but fertilization does not occur, so that the resulting seed is vegetatively produced.

————, **facultative.** When sexual and asexual reproduction alternate.

appressed (pressed down). Closely and flatly pressed against.

autogamous. See **self-fertilizing.**

autopolyploidy. A polyploid arising through multiplication of the complete haploid set of a species.

backmutation. See **mutation.**

betalins. A kind of nitrogenous pigment found in the order Centrospermae; it replaces the anthocyanins in that group.

biosystematics. The application of genetics, cytology, statistics, and chemistry to the solution of systematic questions in order to provide explanations about the diversity of organisms within the frame of the theory of evolution.

biosystematy. See **biosystematics.**

breeding population. A reproductive community of sexual and cross-fertilized individuals that share in a common gene pool.

calyx (pl. calyces). The outer whorl of floral envelopes composed of the sepals.

capsule. A dry fruit resulting from the maturing of an ovary formed by more than one carpel.

carbohydrates. Organic compounds with the empirical formula $C_n(H_2O)_n$. Examples of carbohydrates: sugars, starch, cellulose.

carboxyl group. $R\!-\!C\!-\!OH$. A chemical group, characteristically acid, as a
$$\overset{\|}{O}$$
result of the dissociation of the hydroxyl H to form $R\!-\!C\!-\!O^-$
$$\overset{\|}{O}$$

carotenoids. A large group of compounds that constitute the yellow to red fat-soluble pigments of plants.

carpel. One of the foliar ovule-bearing units of a pistil or ovary.

category. Any of the levels in the taxonomic hierarchy, such as species, genus, and so on.

centromere. The constriction in the chromosome that is involved in the movement of the chromosomes to the poles during cell division.

chaff. A small, thin, dry, and membranous scale or bract; in particular the bracts in the flower heads of members of the sunflower family (Compositae).

character. An attribute of an organism resulting from the interaction of a gene or genes with the environment.

———, **continuous.** Said of a character whose variation in the population does not show discontinuities.

———, **discontinuous.** Said of a character whose variation in the population can be broken down into discrete classes.

———, **qualitative.** See **discontinuous character.**

———, **quantitative.** See **continuous character.**

——— **state.** Any of the values that a particular character can have. Used particularly when referring to discontinuous characters.

chiasma. An exchange of partners between paired chromatids in the first division of meiosis.

chromatid. One of two threadlike structures formed by the longitudinal division of a chromosome during meiotic prophase and known as daughter chromosomes during anaphase.

chromatin. General term used to refer to the chromosome substances that stain with such dyes as acetocarmine or acetoorcein. The nucleoprotein complex of the chromosomes.

chromosomes. Structural units of the nucleus that carry the genes in linear order.

classification. The ordering of plants (or any other objects) into classes or groups.

clone. A group of individuals resulting from vegetative multiplication; any plant propagated vegetatively and therefore presumably a duplicate of its parents.

colchicine. An alkaloid that is used to break the mitotic or meiotic spindle for better observation of the chromosomes.

corolla. Inner circle, or second whorl, of floral envelopes formed by petals.

crossing-over. The exchange of corresponding segments between chromatids of homologous chromosomes during meiotic prophase. Its genetic consequence is the recombination of linked genes.

cytokinesis. The process of cell division as contrasted with the division of the chromosomes and the nucleus.

cytology. The study of the cell.

Δ(statistics, calculus) **Delta.** Symbol usually used to denote very small change.

denaturing (of proteins). The loss of the native configuration of a macro-molecule resulting, for instance, from heat treatment, extreme pH changes, chemical treatment, and so on. It is usually accompanied by loss of biological activity.

diakinesis. The last stage of the prophase of meiosis. During diakinesis chromosomes usually can be observed very well under the microscope.

dicline. Unisexual; requiring two flowers to represent both sexes.

dioecious. Of plants in which staminate (male) and pistillate (female) flowers occur on different individuals.

diploid. The chromosome state in which each type of chromosome except for the sex chromosomes is always represented twice.

disk flower (in Compositae). The tubular flowers in the center of the flowering heads of most members of the sunflower family (Compositae).

disulfide bond. R—S—S—R. A bond between two S ions.

DNA. Deoxyribonucleic acid. A polymer of deoxyribonucleotides. The genetic material of all cells and most viruses.

dominant (gene). Intra-allelic interaction causing one allele to manifest itself more or less, when heterozygous, than its alternate allele.

ecological race. See **ecotype.**

ecotype. A group of populations that share certain physiological and genetic characteristics that make them better adapted to the ecological conditions of an area than other populations of the species.

embryo-sac mother cell. The cell that through meiosis and subsequent mitosis gives rise to the embryo sac.

endopolyploidy. Increase in the chromosome number of vegetative cells.

environment. The sum total of the external conditions that affect growth and development of an organism.

epistasis. Dominance of one gene over a nonallelic gene. The gene suppressed is said to be *hypostatic.* More generally the term *epistasis* is used to describe all types of interallelic interaction whereby manifestation at any locus is affected by genetic phase at any or all other loci.

family (nomenclature). A required category formed by one or more genera. (genetics) A group of individuals directly related by descent from a common ancestor.

fitness. The ability to produce fertile offspring that survive to reproductive age. Also called *Darwinian fitness.*

———, **immediate.** The ability of a population to produce fertile offspring that survive to reproductive age in the immediately next generation.

flexibility, long-range. The ability of maintaining a high fitness over a long period of time.

founder principle (Mayr's). The phenomenon by which the gene pool of a newly established population represents only a small portion of the species gene pool.

gametophytic generation. The generation in plants that bears the sex organs; in ferns a small body bearing archegonia and antheridia; in the angiosperms the pollen and pollen tube and the embryo sac and its contents.

gene flow. The transmission of genes from one population to another.

genetic background. The genotype with which a particular gene interacts.

genetic death. Refers to the loss of gametes when one allele is replaced by another in a population.

genetic drift. The phenomenon by which each generation is a random sample of the previous one.

genetic load. The amount by which the average fitness in the population is lower than that of an individual with the optimal (best) genotypic composition.

genetic locus. The position occupied by a gene in a chromosome.

genome. A set of chromosomes corresponding to the haploid set of a species.

genotype. The entire genetic constitution of an organism as distinguished from its physical appearance or phenotype.

genus (nomenclature). A required category formed by one or more species.

glabrous. Not hairy, hairless.

gynodioecious. A plant that has pistillate (female) flowers, and a few bisexual flowers.

haploid. The chromosome state in which each chromosome is present only once.

heterochromatin. The dark-staining areas of a chromosome. The chemical and physical properties of heterochromatin are still very much debated.

heterokaryon. A mycelium of a fungus with two or more genetically different nuclei within each cell.

heteromorphic. With more than one form.

heterosis. Hybrid vigor that causes an F_1 hybrid to fall outside the range of the parents with respect to some character or characters. Usually applied to size, rate of growth, or general fitness, although in strict terms it should be applied only to fitness, and the term *luxuriance* used to denote size or rate of growth.

heterozygous. Having unlike alleles at one or more corresponding loci (opposite of homozygous).

hispid. Provided with stiff and bristly hairs.

homeologous (chromosomes). Chromosomes that have homologous segments and may pair at meiosis, but are not homologous along their entire length. Usually belonging to different species.

homogametic. Producing only one kind of gamete.

homologous (chromosome). Chromosomes that pair (synapse) along their entire length in meiotic prophase.

——— (segments). Parts of chromosomes that pair (synapse) in meiotic prophase.

homomorphic. Having only one form.

homozygous. Having like alleles at corresponding loci on homologous chromosomes. An organism can be homozygous at one or many loci.

hybrid superiority. See **heterosis.**

hydrogen bond. A weak attractive force between one electronegative atom and a hydrogen atom that is covalently linked to a second electronegative atom.

hydrophobic bond. The association of nonpolar groups with each other in aqueous solutions, arising because of the tendency of water molecules to exclude nonpolar molecules.

hypostasis (hypostatic). Recessiveness of a gene with respect to a nonallelic gene. The converse of *epistasis*.

immediate fitness. See **fitness.**

inbreeding. The mating of individuals more closely related than individuals mating at random. The mating of a plant with itself.

incompatibility alleles. The series of genes, usually referred to as *S* alleles, that prevent the pollen of certain plants from germinating on the style of the same plant that produced the pollen.

internodes. The part of a stem between two nodes, or joints, where leaves are borne.

introgression. See **introgressive hybridization.**

introgressive hybridization. The introduction into one species, through back-crosses following upon an interspecific cross, of genes of another species.

inversion (chromosomal). A rearrangement of a chromosome segment so that its genes are in reversed linear order (see Fig. 9–8).

involucral bracts. The bracts that surround the flowering head in the sun-flower family (Compositae).

ionic bond. The electrostatic forces acting between oppositely charged ionic chemical groups.

isolating mechanism. Any of many structures or phenomena that separate one plant (or population) from another so that mating between them is prevented (Table 7–1).

karyology. The study of the cell nucleus.

karyotype. The chromosomal complex characteristic of a group of allied plants, associated with both morphology and number of chromosomes.

linkage. The phenomenon when genes are located on the same chromosome and therefore tend to be transmitted together in the gametes.

locus. See **genetic locus.**

long-range flexibility. See **flexibility.**

Mayr's founder principle. See **founder principle.**

meiosis. The process by which a diploid cell gives rise through two consecutive divisions to four haploid spores.

meristem. Undifferentiated tissue whose cells are capable of developing into various organs or tissues.

metaphase. The second stage of cell division, in which the chromosomes align in the middle of the cell plate prior to separation(or division) and movement to the poles.

microsporocytes. The cells that give rise by meiotic division to the smaller of two kinds of spores. In the angiosperms the cells (pollen mother cells) that give rise by meiosis to the pollen.

mitosis. The process by which the nucleus of a somatic cell divides into two nuclei with the same number of chromosomes as the mother cell. Mitosis is usually followed by cytokinesis.

modifier (genes). Genes that affect the expression of a nonallelic gene or genes.

monoecious. Of the population or species that has plants with staminate (male) flowers and pistillate (female) flowers, on the same plant.

monoecious dicline. Of the population or species that has the staminate (male) flowers and pistillate flowers borne on the same plant but on separate flowers.

monomorphic. Having only one form.

morphology. The study of the form of plants.

multiple factors. See **multiple gene systems.**

multiple gene systems. Systems of genes whose effects are too slight to be identified individually but that through similar and supplementary effects can have important effects on total variability.

mutation. A sudden inheritable variation in a gene or in chromosome structure. The product is called a *mutant gene.*

—— **backmutation.** A mutation of a mutant gene to its original state.

——, **recurrent.** A mutation that occurs regularly in a population.

mutator genotype. A genotype in which mutations occur at a very high frequency.

natural selection. The non-random differential reproduction of genotypes.

nomenclature. The application of distinct names to each of the groups recognized in a classification.

ontogeny. The development cycle of an individual.

outbreeding. The habitual crossing with another plant.

pachytene. The third stage of meiotic prophase, when homologous chromosomes pair and crossing-over takes place.

papilionate flower. The pealike (butterflylike) flower of the tribe Papilionoideae of the pea family (Leguminosae).

pappus (Compositae). Peculiar modified calyx borne on the upper part of the ovary and persisting in the fruit; it can be plumose, bristlelike, and so on, and aids in seed dispersal.

peptide bond. A covalent bond between two amino acids in which the alpha amino group of one amino acid is bonded to the alpha carboxyl group of the other with the elimination of water.

petiole. The leaf stalk, missing in some leaves.

phenetic. Relation of similarity of characters, as opposed to phylogenetic, or similarity of descent.

phenotype. Appearance of an organism, the result of the development of the genetic message contained in the genotype in a particular environment.

phylogeny. The evolutionary history of a population, species, or higher category. Also used when referring to the evolutionary history of a structure or organ.

physiology (plant). The study of the function of plants.

pin. The long-styled form in a distylous, heterostylous form.

pleiotropy. The effect of one gene on more than one phenotypic character.

pollen mother cells. See **microsporocytes.**

polygamodioecious. A plant that has unisexual flowers and a few bisexual flowers.

polygenes. See **multiple gene systems.**

polymer. A regular, covalently bonded arrangement of basic subunits called *monomers,* which is produced by the repetitive action of one or a few chemical reactions.

polypeptide. A polymer of amino acids linked together by peptide bonds.

polyploid. A plant with a chromosome complement of three or more sets of chromosomes, each with the exact haploid number.

population. See **breeding population.**

protandry. Maturing of the anthers before the style, which usually impedes self-fertilization.

protogyny. Maturing of the styles before the anthers, which usually impedes self-fertilization.

pubescent. Covered with short soft hairs, downy.

radioactive isotope. An isotope of an element that emits ionizing radiation because its nucleus is unstable.

ray flower. Outer flower with a straplike corolla in the flowering head of some members of the sunflower family (Compositae).

recessive (gene). The member of an allelic pair that is not expressed when the other (dominant) member occupies the homologous chromosome.

recombination. Formation of new combinations of genes as a result of the sexual process; the appearance of new combinations of traits in the off-spring; also applied sometimes to the process of hybridization between members of the same population and species.

recurrent mutation. See **mutation.**

relationship. A statement about two or more objects that is either true or false.

ribonuclease. The enzyme that acts on RNA (ribose Nucleic acid) as a substrate.

self-compatibility. Capability of producing seeds when the style is dusted with pollen from the same plant.

self-incompatibility. Genetic incapacity of producing seed when the style is dusted with pollen from the same plant.

sessile. Not stalked, sitting.

shift (chromosome). The shifting of a chromosome segment to another position with the same chromosome.

sibling species. Species that are morphologically identical or nearly identical in their phenotypes.

species (nomenclature). The basic required unit of the taxonomic system, below the rank of genus. For further discussion see Chapter 7.

sporophyte generation. The generation that produces the spores. In ferns and seed plants the foliaceous vegetative plant, as opposed to the **gametophyte.**

stochastic. Pertaining to conjecture; of a process that cannot be predicted exactly, no matter how accurate the information.

sympatric. Said of taxa whose geographical ranges overlap.

systematics. The branch of biology concerned with the comparative study of organisms and all relationships among them.

taxon. A general term applied to the organisms in any taxonomic element: population, species, genus, and so on, irrespective of the category in which it is placed.

taxonomy. The study of classification, its principles, procedures, and rules.

tetraploid. A polyploid with exactly four sets of basic (haploid) chromosomes.

thrums. The short-styled form, in a distylous heterostylous species.

translocation. Change in position of a chromosome segment to a position in a different chromosome.

———, **nonreciprocal.** When only one segment is exchanged between two chromosomes.

———, **reciprocal.** When both the donor and the recipient chromosome exchange segments.

trinucleate. Having three nuclei.

trophic. Pertaining to a relation of dependence, such as herbivorous animals' dependence on plants, carnivores' dependence on herbivores, and so on.

univalent (chromosome). A chromosome that during meiotic pachytene does not pair.

zygote. First cell of an organism, formed by the union of two gametes, from which in multicellular organisms the whole individual will develop.

Bibliography

ADAMS, H., and E. ANDERSON, 1958. A conspectus of hybridization in the Orchidaceae. *Evolution*, 12: 512–518.

ALLARD, R. W., 1960. *Principles of Plant Breeding*. New York.

—— 1965. Genetic systems associated with colonizing ability in predominantly self-pollinated species. In *The Genetics of Colonizing Species*, H. G. Baker and G. L. Stebbins (eds.). New York.

—— and P. E. HANSCHE, 1965. Population and biometrical genetics in plant breeding. *Proc. 11th. Int. Congr. Genetics*, 3: 665–679.

ALSTON, R., 1965. A symposium on macromolecular evolution: a systematic perspective. *BioScience* 15: 466–468.

—— and B. L. TURNER, 1963a. Natural hybridization among four species of Baptisia. *Amer. Jour. Bot.* 50: 159–173.

—— 1963b. *Biochemical Systematics*. New York.

——, R. N. LESTER, and D. HORNE, 1962. Chromatographic validation of two morphologically similar hybrids of different origins. *Science* 137: 1048–1050.

ANDERSON, E., 1949. *Introgressive Hybridization*. New York.

—— 1952. *Plants, Man and Life*. Boston.

—— 1953. Introgressive hybridization. *Biological Reviews* 28: 280–307.

—— and B. ANDERSON, 1954. Introgression of Salvia apiana and Salvia mellifera. *Ann. Mo. Bot. Gard.* 41: 329–338.

APIRION, D., and D. ZOHARY, 1961. Chlorophyll lethal in natural populations of the orchard grass (*Dactylis glomerata* L.). A case of balanced polymorphism in plants. *Genetics* 46: 393–399.

ARBER, A., 1928. *Herbals, Their Origin and Evolution*, 2nd. ed. London.

AVERY, O. T., C. M. MCLEOD, and M. MCCARTY, 1944. Studies on the chemical nature of the substance inducing transformation of hemococcal types. *Jour. Exp. Medicine* 79: 137–158.

BAKER, H. G., 1948. Dimorphism and monomorphism in the Plumbaginaceae I: a survey of the family. *Ann. Bot. II*, 12: 207–219.

—— 1953a. Dimorphism and monomorphism in the Plumbaginaceae III: correlation of geographical distribution patterns with dimorphism and monomorphism in Limonium. *Ann. Bot. II*, 17: 615–627.

—— 1953b. Race formation and reproductive method in the flowering plants. *Symposia Soc. Exptl. Biol.* 7: 114–145.

—— 1954. Dimorphism and incompatibility in the Plumbaginaceae. *8ème Congr. Int. Bot., Paris, Rapp. et Comm., Sert*, 10: 133–134.

—— 1955. Self-compatibility and establishment after "long distance" dispersal. *Evolution* 9: 347–348.

—— 1963. Evolutionary mechanisms in pollination biology. *Science* 139: 877–883.

BARNES, B. V., 1961. Hybrid aspens in the lower peninsula of Michigan. *Rhodora* 63: 311–324.

BATEMAN, A. J., 1952. Self-incompatibility systems in angiosperms. I. Theory. *Heredity* 6: 285–310.

213

BECKMAN, L., J. G. SCANDALIOS, and J. L. BREWBAKER, 1964. Genetics of leucine aminopeptidase isozymes in maize. *Genetics* **50**:899–904.

BERRIE, G. K., 1955. Chromosomes of African hepatics. *Jubalae. Brit. Bryol. Soc. Trans.* **2**:532–636.

BJÖRKMAN, O., 1966. Comparative studies of photosynthesis and respiration in ecological races. *Brittonia* **18**:214–224.

BRADSHAW, A. D., 1959. Population differentiation in Agrostis tenuis Sibth: I. Morphological differences. *New Phytol.* **58**:208–227.

────── 1960. Population differentiation in Agrostis tenuis Sibth: III. Populations in varied environments. *New Phytol.* **59**:92–103.

────── 1962. The taxonomic problems of local geographical variation in plant species. *Taxonomy and Geograph. Syst., Assoc. Publ.* **4**:7–16.

──────, T. S. McNEILLY, and R. P. GREGORY, 1965. Industrialization, evolution, and the development of heavy metal tolerance in plants. *Brit. Ecol. Soc. Symp.* **6**:327–343.

BRITTEN, R. J., and D. E. KOHNE, 1968. Repeated Sequences in DNA. *Science* **161**: 529–540.

CAMP, W. H., and C. L. GILLY, 1943. The structure and origin of species. *Brittonia* **4**:323–385.

CARSON, H. L., 1957. The species as a field for gene recombination. In *The Species Problem*, E Mayr (ed.). Washington.

────── 1967. Inbreeding the gene fixation in natural populations. In *Heritage from Mendel*, R. A. Brink (ed.). Madison, Wis.

CLAUSEN, J., 1926. Genetical and cytological investigations on Viola tricolor L. and V. arvensis Murr. *Hereditas* **8**:1–156.

────── and W. HIESEY, 1958. Experimental studies on the nature of species: IV. Genetic structure of ecological races. *Carnegie Inst. Wash. Publ. 615.*

──────, D. D. KECK, and W. HIESEY, 1940. Experimental studies on the nature of species: I. Effects of varied environments on western North American plants. *Carnegie Inst. Wash. Publ. 520.*

────── 1945. Experimental studies on the nature of species: II. Plant evolution through amphiploidy and autopolyploidy with examples from the Madiinae. *Carnegie Inst. Wash. Publ. 564.*

────── 1947. Heredity of geographically and ecologically isolated races. *Amer. Nat.* **81**:114–133.

────── 1948. Experimental studies on the nature of species: III. Environmental responses of climatic races of Achillea. *Carnegie Inst. Wash. Publ. 581.*

CORRENS, C., 1928. Bestimmung, Vererbung, und Verteilung des Geschlechtes bei den höheren Pflanzen. *Hand. Vererb.* **2**:1–138.

CROWE, L. K., 1964. The evolution of outbreeding in plants: I. The angiosperms. *Heredity* **19**:435–457.

DARLINGTON, C. D., 1939. *The Evolution of Genetic Systems*, 1st. ed. Cambridge, England.

────── 1958. *The Evolution of Genetic Systems*, 2nd. ed. New York.

DARWIN, C., 1877. *The Different Forms of Flowers of Plants of the Same Species.* London.

────── 1888. *The Effects of Cross and Self Fertilization in the Vegetable Kingdom.* London.

DAWSON, G. W. P. *An Introduction to the Cytogenetics of Polyploids.* Oxford.

DECKER, J. P., 1959. Some effects of temperature and carbon dioxide concentration on photosynthesis of Mimulus. *Plant Physiology* **34**:103–106.

DOBZHANSKY, T., 1937. What is a species? *Scientia* **61**:280–286.

────── 1950. Mendelian populations and their evolution. *The Amer. Nat.* **84**:401–418.

────── and B. SPASSKY, 1963. Genetics of natural populations: XXXIV. Adaptive norm, genetic load, and genetic elite in Drosophila pseudoobscura. *Genetics* **48**:1467–1485.

DULBERGER, R., 1964. Flower dimorphism and self-incompatibility in Narcissus tazetta. L. *Evolution* **18**:361–363.

EAST, E. N., 1916. Studies in size inheritance in Nicotiana. *Genetics* **1**:164–176.

———— 1929. Self-sterility. *Bibliogr. Genetica* **5**:331–370.

———— 1940. The distribution of self-sterility in flowering plants. *Proc. Amer. Philos. Soc.* **82**:449–518.

———— and A. J. MANGELSDORF, 1925. A new interpretation of the hereditary behavior of self-sterile plants. *P. N. A. S.* **11**:116–183.

EMERSON, R. A., and E. N. EAST, 1913. The inheritance of quantitative characters in maize. *Nebraska Agr. Exp. Station Res. Bull. 2*.

EMERSON, S. H., 1952. Biochemical models of heterosis in Neurospora. In *Heterosis*, J. W. Growen (ed.). Ames, Iowa.

EPLING, C., 1947a. Natural hybridization of Salvia apiana and S. mellifera. *Evolution* **1**:69–78.

———— 1947b. Actual and potential gene flow in natural populations. *Amer. Nat.* **81**:104–113.

———— and T. DOBZHANSKY, 1942. Micrographic races of Linanthus parryae. *Genetics* **27**:317–332.

————, H. LEWIS, and F. M. BALL, 1960. The breeding group and seed storage: a study in population dynamics. *Evolution* **14**:238–255.

FISHER, R. A., 1936. Has Mendel's work been rediscovered? *Ann. Sci.* **1**:115–137.

FITCH, W. M., and E. MARGOLIASH, 1966. Construction of phylogenetic trees. *Science* **155**:279–284.

FRYXELL, P. A., 1957. Mode of reproduction of higher plants. *Bot. Rev.* **23**:135–233.

GOTTLIEB, L., 1968. Hybridization between Arctostaphylos viscida and A. canescens in Oregon. *Brittonia* **20**:83–93.

GRANT, K. A., and V. GRANT, 1964. Mechanical isolation of Salvia apiana and S. mellifera (Labiatae). *Evolution* **18**:196–212.

GRANT, V., 1952. Isolation and hybridization between Aquilegia formosa and A. pubescens. *Aliso* **2**:341–360.

———— 1958. The regulation of recombination in plants. *Cold Spring Harbor Symp. Quant. Biol.* **23**:337–363.

———— 1963. *The Origin of Adaptations*. New York.

———— 1964a. The biological composition of a taxonomic species in Gilia. *Adv. in Genetics* **12**:281–327.

———— 1964b. *The Architecture of the Germ Plasm*. New York.

———— 1967. Linkage between morphology and viability in plant species. *Am. Nat.* **101**:125–140.

GREENE, E. L., 1909. *Landmarks of Botanical History*. New York.

HAGBERG, A., 1953. Heterozygosity in erectoides mutations in barley. *Hereditas* **39**:161–178.

HAGERUP, O., 1950. Rain pollination. *Kgl. Danske Vid. Selsk. Biol. Meddel.* **18**:1–19.

———— 1951. Pollination in the Faroes—in spite of rain and poverty of insects. *Kgl. Danske Vid. Selsk. Biol. Meddel.* **18**:3–48.

HARLAN, J., and DE WET, 1963. The compilospecies concept. *Evolution* **17**:497–501.

HEISER, C. B., 1947. Hybridization between the sunflower species Helianthus annuus and H. petiolaris. *Evolution* **1**:249–262.

———— 1949. Study in the evolution of the sunflower species Helianthus annuus and H. bolanderi. *Univ. Calif. Publ. Bot.* **23**:157–208.

———— 1951a. Hybridization in the annual sunflowers: Helianthus annuus × H. debilis var. cucumerifolius. *Evolution* **5**:42–51.

———— 1951b. The sunflower among the North-American Indians. *Proc. Am. Phil. Soc.* **95**:432–448.

HEISER, C. B., 1954. Variation and subspeciation in the common sunflower Helianthus annuus. *Am. Midl. Nat.* **51**:287–305.

—— 1961. Natural hybridization and introgression with particular reference to Helianthus. *Recent Adv. in Botany* **1**:874–877.

——, W. C. MARTIN, and D. M. SMITH, 1962. Species crosses in Helianthus: I. Diploid species. *Brittonia* **14**:137–147.

HUNZIKER, J., 1966. Differentiation chromosomica en el complejo hexaploide Agropyron scabriglume. *Kurtziana* **3**:127–149.

——1967. Chromosome and protein differentiation in the Agropyron scabriglume complex. *Taxon* **16**:259–266.

JACKSON, R. C., 1957. New low chromosome number for plants. *Science* **128**:1115–1116.

—— 1962. Interspecific hybridization in Haplopappus and its bearing on chromosome evolution in the Blepharodon section. *Amer. Jour. Bot.* **49**:119–132.

JAIN, S. K., and A. D. BRADSHAW, 1966. Evolutionary divergence among adjacent plant populations: I. The evidence and its theoretical analysis. *Heredity* **21**:407–442.

——, and D. R. MARSHALL, 1967. Population studies in predominantly self-pollinating species: X. Variation in Natural populations of Avena fatua and A. barbata. *Am. Nat.* **101**:19–34.

JOHNSON, B. L., and O. HALL, 1965. Analysis of phylogenetic affinities in the Triticinae by protein electrophoresis. *Amer. Jour. Bot.* **52**:506–513.

JONES, D. F., 1932. Interaction of specific genes determining sex in dioecious maize. *Proc. 6th Intern. Congr. Genetics* (Ithaca, N.Y.) **2**:104–107.

KECK, D. D., 1958. Taxonomic notes on the California flora. *Aliso* **4**:101–114.

KHOSHOO, T. N., 1956. Chromosomes from herbarium sheets in Impatiens. *Stain Techn.* **31**:31–33.

KIHARA, A., and I. HIROYASHI, 1932. Die Geschlechtchromosomen von Humulus. *8th Congr. Japan. Assoc. Advan. Sci.* **61**:363–367.

KRUCKEBERG, A. R., 1951. Intraspecific variability in the response of certain native plant species to serpentine soil. *Amer. Jour. Bot.* **38**:408–419.

—— 1954. The ecology of serpentine soils: III. Plant species in relation to serpentine species. *Ecology* **35**: 267–274.

—— 1957. Variation in fertility of hybrids between isolated populations of the serpentine species, Streptanthus glandulosus Hook. *Evolution* **11**:185–211.

—— 1958. The taxonomy of the species complex Streptanthus glandulosus Hook. *Madroño* **14**:217–248.

KURABAYASHI, M., H. LEWIS, and P. H. RAVEN, 1962. A comparative study of mitosis in the Onagraceae. *Am. Jour. Bot.* **49**:1003–1026.

KYHOS, D. W., 1965. The independent aneuploid origin of two species of Chaenactis (Compositae) from a common ancestor. *Evolution* **19**:26–43.

LAWRENCE, G., 1965. Herbals: their history and significance. In *History of Botany*. Clark Memorial Library, Los Angeles.

LERNER, M., 1958. *The Genetic Basis of Selection*. New York.

LEWIS, D., 1942. The evolution of sex in flowering plants. *Biol. Rev.* **17**:46–67.

—— 1954. Comparative incompatibility in angiosperms and fungi. *Adv. Genetics* **6**:235–285.

—— 1955. Sexual incompatibility. *Sci. Progress* **172**:593–605.

LEWIS, H., 1961. Experimental sympatric populations of Clarkia. *Am. Nat.* **45**:155–168.

—— 1962. Catastrophic selection as a factor in speciation. *Evolution* **16**:257–271.

—— and P. H. RAVEN, 1958a. Clarkia franciscana, a new species from central California. *Brittonia* **10**:7–13.

—— 1958b. Rapid evolution in Clarkia. *Evolution* **12**:319–336.

—— and M. R. ROBERTS, 1956. The origin of Clarkia lingulata. *Evolution* **10**:126–138.

LEWIS, W., R. L. OLIVER, and Y. SUALA, 1967. Cytogeography of Claytonia virginiana and its allies. *Ann. Mo. Bot. Gard.* **54**:153–171.

LLOYD, D. G., 1965. Evolution of self-compatibility and racial differentiation in Leavenworthia (Cruciferae). *Contr. Gray Herb.* **195**:1–135.

LÖVQUIST, B., 1956. The Cardamine pratensis complex. *Symbolae Bot. Upsalienses* **14**:1–131.

MACMILLAN, C., 1959. The role of ecotypic variation in the distribution of the central grassland of North America. *Ecol. Monogr.* **29**:285–308.

────── 1964. Ecotypic differentiation within four North American prairie grasses: I. Morphological variation within transplanted community fractions. *Amer. Jour. Bot.* **51**:1119–1128.

────── 1965. Ecotypic differentiation within four North American prairie grasses: II. Behavioral variation within transplanted community fractions. *Amer. Jour. Bot.* **52**: 55–65.

MATHER, K., 1949. *Biometrical Genetics*. New York.

MAYR, E., 1942. *Systematics and the Origin of Species*. New York.

────── 1947. Ecological factors in speciation. *Evolution* **1**:263–288.

────── 1957. Species concepts and definitions. In *The Species Problem*, E. Mayr (ed.). Washington.

────── 1963. *Animal Species and Evolution*. Cambridge, Mass.

McNAUGHTON, S. J., 1965. Differential enzymatic activity in ecological races of Typha latifolia L. *Science* **150**:1829–1830.

MILNER, H. W., and W. M. HIESEY, 1964a. Photosynthesis in climatic races of Mimulus: I. Effect of light intensity and temperature on rate. *Plant Physiology* **39**:208–213.

────── 1964b. Photosynthesis in climatic races of Mimulus: II. Effect of time and CO_2 concentration on rate. *Plant Physiology* **39**:746–750.

MOONEY, H. A., 1967. Influence of soil type on the distribution of two closely related species of Erigeron. *Ecology* **47**:950–958.

MULCAHY, D. L., 1967. The selective advantage of staminate heterogamy. *Taxon* **16**:280–283.

MULLER, C. H., 1952. Ecological control of hybridization in Quercus: a factor in the mechanism of evolution? *Evolution* **6**:147–161.

MUNZ, P., 1959. *A California Flora*. Berkeley, Calif.

NILSSON-EHLE, H., 1909. Kreuzungsuntersuchungen an Hafer und Weizen. Lunds Univ.

NINAN, C. A., 1958. Studies on the cytology and phylogeny of the pteridophytes: VI. Observations on the Ophioglossaceae. *Cytologia* **23**:291–315.

NIRENBERG, M. W., O. W. JONES, P. LEDER, B. C. CLARK, W. S. SLY, and S. PESTKA, 1963. On the coding of genetic information. *Cold Spring Harbor Symp. Quant. Biol.* **28**:549–551.

────── , and J. H. MATTHAEI, 1961. The dependence of cell-free protein synthesis in E. coli upon naturally occurring or synthetic polyribonucleotides. *P. N. A. S.* **47**:1588–1602.

ORNDUFF, R., 1966. A biosystematic survey of the goldfield genus Lasthenia. *Univ. Calif. Publ. Botany* **40**:1–92.

PANDEY, K. K., 1960. Evolution of gametophytic and sporophytic systems of self-incompatibility in angiosperms. *Evolution* **14**:98–115.

PRAZMO, W., 1960. Genetic studies on the genus Aquilegia, I. *Acta Polsk. Tovarz. Bot.* **29**:57–77.

────── 1961. Genetic studies on the genus Aquilegia, II. *Acta Polsk. Tovarz. Bot.* **30**:421–442.

QUARTERMAN, E., 1950. Major plant communities of Tennessee cedar glades. *Ecology* **31**:234–254.

RAVEN, P., 1962. The systematics of Oenothera subgenus Chylismia. *Univ. Calif. Publ. Bot.* **34**:1–122.

RAVEN, P., 1964. The generic subdivision of Onagraceae, tribe Onagreae. *Brittonia* **16**:276–288.

—— and H. THOMPSON, 1964. Haploidy and angiosperm evolution. *Am. Nat.* **98**:251–252.

RAY, P., and H. F. CHISAKI, 1957. Studies on Amsinkia II. Relationships among primitive species. *Amer. Jour. Bot.* **44**:537–544.

RILEY, H. P., 1936. The genetics and physiology of self-sterility in the genus Capsella. *Genetics* **21**:24–39.

RILEY, R., and V. CHAPMAN, 1958. Genetic control of the cytologically diploid behavior of hexaploid wheat. *Nature* **182**:713–715.

—— and C. N. LAW, 1965. Genetic variation in chromosome pairing. *Advanc. in Genetics* **13**:57–114.

ROLLINS, R. C., 1958. The genetic evaluation of a taxonomic character in Dithryea (Cruciferae). *Rhdora* **60**:145–152.

—— 1963. The evolution and systematics of Leavenworthia (Cruciferae). *Contr. Gray Herb.* **192**:1–98.

RÜDENBERG, L., and O. T. SOLBRIG, 1963. Chromosome number and morphology in the genus Gutierrezia (Compositae-Astereae). *Phyton* **20**:199–204.

SAX, K., 1922. Sterility in wheat hybrids: II. Chromosome behavior in partially sterile hybrids. *Genetics* **7**:513–552.

—— 1933. Species hybrids in Platanus and Campsis. *Jour. Arnold Arboretum* **14**:274–278.

SCHNACK, B., and G. COVAS, 1945. Hibridación interespecifica en Glandularia (Verbenaceae). *Darwiniana* **7**:71–79.

—— and O. T. SOLBRIG, 1953. El hibrido Glandularia laciniata × G. peruviana y su anfidiploide artificial. *Rev. Fac. Agronomia* (La Plata) **29**:255–266.

SEHGAL, S. M., 1963. Effects of teosinte and Tripsacum introgression in maize. *Bussey Institution Publ.*, Cambridge, Mass.

SHULL, G. H., 1914. Duplicate genes for capsule form in Bursa bursa-pastoris. *Zeitschr. Ind. Abst. Vererb.* **12**:97–149.

SIMPSON, G. G., 1961. *Principles of Animal Taxonomy*. New York.

——, A. ROE, and R. C. LEWONTIN, 1960. *Quantitative Zoology*. New York.

SINNOT, E. W., and G. B. DURHAM, 1922. Inheritance in the summer squash. *Jour. Heredity* **13**:177–186.

SMITH, B., 1963. The mechanism of sex determination in Rumex hastatulus. *Genetics* **48**:1265–1288.

—— 1964. The evolving karyotype of Rumex hastatulus. *Evolution* **18**:93–104.

SNYDER, L. A., 1950. Morphological variability and hybrid development in Elymus glaucus. *Amer. Jour. Bot.* **37**:628–636.

—— 1951. Cytology of inter-strain hybrids and the probable origin of variability in Elymus glaucus. *Amer. Jour. Bot.* **38**:195–202.

SOKAL, R., and P. SNEATH, 1963. *Principles of Numerical Taxonomy*. San Francisco.

SOLBRIG. O. T., 1964. Infraspecific variation in the Gutierrezia sarothrae complex (Compositae-Astereae). *Contr. Gray Herb.* **193**:67–115.

—— 1966a. *Evolution and Systematics*. New York.

—— 1966b. Rol de la polinización zoofila en la evolución de las angiospermas. *Bol. Soc. Argentina de Bot.* **11**:1–18.

—— 1968. Fertility, sterility, and the species problem. In *Modern Methods in Plant Taxonomy*, V. H. Heywood (ed.), London.

——, C. PASSANI, and R. GLASS, 1968. Artificial hybridization between different polyploid levels in Glandularia. *Amer. Jour. Bot.* **55**:1235–1239.

STEBBINS, G. L., 1947. Types of polyploids: their classification and significance. *Advanc. in Genet.* **1**:403–429.

STEBBINS, G. L., 1950. *Variation and Evolution in Plants*. New York.

—— 1957. Self-fertilization and population variability in the higher plants. *Am. Nat.* **91**:337–354.

—— 1958. The inviability, weakness, and sterility of interspecific hybrids. *Advanc. in Genet.* **8**:147–215.

—— 1959. Genes, chromosomes, and evolution. In *Vistas in Botany*, W. Turrill (ed.). London.

STURTEVANT, A. H., 1965. *A History of Genetics*. New York.

SUNESON, C. A., 1949. Survival of four barley varieties in a mixture. *Agron. Jour.* **41**:459–461.

THODAY, J. M., and T. B. BOAM, 1959. Effects of disruptive selection: II. Polymorphism and divergence without isolation. *Heredity* **13**:205–218.

TURESON, G., 1922. The species and the variety as ecological units. *Hereditas* **3**:100–113.

—— 1925. The plant species in relation to habitat and climate. *Hereditas* **6**:147–236.

—— 1929. Zur Natur und Begrenzung der Artenheiten. *Hereditas* **12**:323–334.

U, N., 1935. Genome analysis in Brassica with special reference to the experimental formation of B. napus and peculiar mode of fertilization. *Jap. Jour. Bot.* **7**:389–462.

VUILLEUMIER, B., 1967. The origin and evolutionary development of heterostyly in the angiosperms. *Evolution* **21**:210–226.

WAGNER, M., 1868. *Die Darwinische Theorie und das Migrationgesetz der Organismen*. Leipzig.

WATSON, J. D., 1965. *Molecular Biology of the Gene*. New York.

—— and F. H. C. CRICK, 1953. Molecular structure of nucleic acids. A structure for deoxyribose nucleic acid. *Nature* **171**:737–738.

WATSON, P., and J. CLAUSEN, 1961. Phenotypic responses to contrasting environments in the genus Poa. *Scottish Plant Breeding Station Report*.

WESTERGAARD, M., 1958. The mechanism of sex determination in dioecious flowering plants. *Advanc. Genet.* **9**:217–281.

WILSON, E. O., 1965. The challenge from related species. In *The Genetics of Colonizing Species*, H. G. Baker and G. L. Stebbins (eds.). New York.

WINGE, Ö., 1940. Taxonomic and evolutionary studies in Erophila based on cytogenetic investigations. *Compt. Rend. Trav. Lab. Carlsberg Ser. Physiol.* **23**:41–74.

WOODWORTH, C. M., E. R. LENG, and R. W. JUGENHEIMER, 1952. Fifty generations of selection for protein and oil in corn. *Agron. Jour.* **44**:60–65.

Index

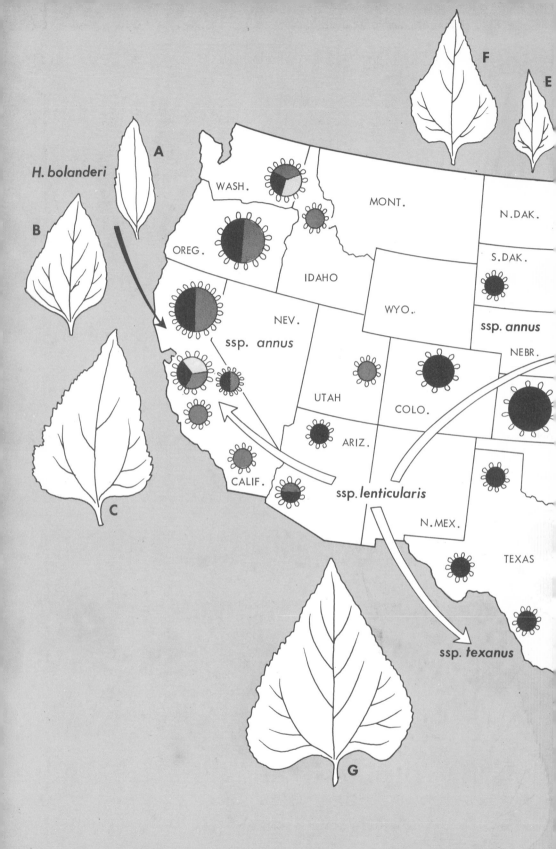

H. bolanderi

A
B
C
F
E
G

WASH.
OREG.
IDAHO
MONT.
N.DAK.
S.DAK.
ssp. *annus*
NEV.
WYO.
NEBR.
ssp. *annus*
UTAH
COLO.
ssp. *lenticularis*
CALIF.
ARIZ.
N.MEX.
TEXAS
ssp. *texanus*